INVESTIGATING
DIGITAL ELECTRONICS

INVESTIGATING
DIGITAL ELECTRONICS
. . . .

R. HIGGINS
A. J. C. MAY

Longman
Scientific &
Technical

Longman Scientific & Technical
Longman Group UK Limited,
Longman House, Burnt Mill, Harlow,
Essex CM20 2JE, England
and Associated Companies throughout the world.

First published 1991

British Library Cataloguing in Publication Data
  Higgins, R.
    Investigating digital electronics.
    1. Electronics
    I. Title   II. May, A. J. C.
    621.3815

Produced by Longman Group (FE) Limited

Printed in Hong Kong

ISBN 0 582 06004.4

CONTENTS
. . . .

PREFACE

. . . .

This book is intended for readers who have completed Book One *Investigating electronics* or readers with some basic electronic knowledge.

The book is divided into three parts, introducing:

Logic gates
Multivibrators and
Digital microelectronics

The two books *Investigating electronics* and *Investigating digital electronics* give an adequate cover of the EITB TR21 basic training requirement in electronics and groups who may find it useful include those studying 'Design and Technology' in schools and students taking BTEC Engineering courses having a practical electronics content designed to meet the 'common skills' element of their course.

The authors would like to thank the publishers for their friendly co-operation and helpful advice in preparing this book. They would also like to add a word of thanks to their wives, Yvonne and Joan, for their patience, help and encouragement during the preparation of this book.

Roy Higgins
Tony May
1990

ACKNOWLEDGEMENTS

· ·

We are indebted to the following for permission to use copyright material:

Engineering Industry Training Board for one figure from *Assembling Microelectronic Devices to Printed Circuit Boards* (see our page 53); R.S. Components for material from various data sheets and Macmillan Inc. for Figs 3.7, 4.5, 4.8, 4.12 and 4.13 from *Understanding Digital Electronics* by Gene McWhorter (see our pages 68, 69, 71, 78 and 79).

The authors would also like to acknowledge the following help received:

Mr J. Hargreaves for permission to use the facilities of Training 2000 to develop the ideas put forward in the book. Also the staff and students of Training 2000 who encouraged and helped in the production of the book.

Part 1
Logic Gates

DIODE TRANSISTOR LOGIC (DTL)

. . . .

Introduction

One group of logic gates uses a transistor as its basis.

► When the base voltage is higher than that of the emitter, a small current flows from the base to the emitter.

► When a base to emitter current flows, the high-resistance region between the collector and the emitter breaks down and current flows from the supply into the collector and out of the emitter.

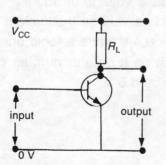

► A load resistor R_L is used to form a voltage divider with the collector/emitter resistance of the transistor. A 1 kΩ resistor is often used for R_L.

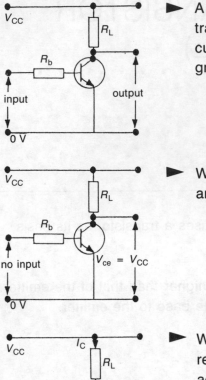

▶ A base resistor R_b is used to limit the base current to the transistor to avoid damaging the transistor with excess current. The value of R_b is made a minimum of ten times greater than the value of R_L.

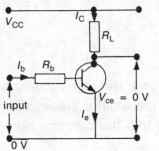

▶ With no base current, the resistance of the output is large and the voltage V_{ce} is almost equal to V_{CC}.

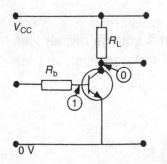

▶ When a base current flows the output resistance falls reducing the output voltage and increasing the voltage across R_L. When I_b is sufficiently large, the transistor is said to be switched on, reducing the output resistance and hence the output voltage to almost zero.

NOT gates

▶ The circuit shown is called a *NOT gate* and is one of a family of logic gates. A transistor switches on, producing an output of about 0 V, when a base voltage of about 0.7 V or over exists. A logic zero is a voltage insufficient to switch on a gate usually below 0.4 V while a logic one must be sufficiently high to switch on a gate or number of gates and is usually between 2 V and 5 V.

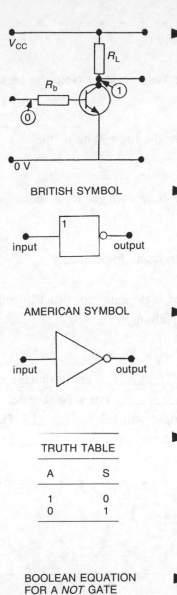

BRITISH SYMBOL

input ─── output

AMERICAN SYMBOL

input ─── output

TRUTH TABLE	
A	S
1	0
0	1

BOOLEAN EQUATION FOR A *NOT* GATE
$$S = \overline{A}$$

► When the base voltage is less than 0.7 V, the transistor is switched off and the collector voltage approaches V_{CC}. This output is called logic 1 and the input voltage of about 0 V is called logic 0. This gate is called a NOT gate because if the input is a 1 then the output is 'not 1' and if the input is a 0 the output is 'not 0'.

► To simplify drawing circuit diagrams, each logic gate has its own symbol which does not show the supply or 0 V connections, though it is necessary to connect them to a supply in practice. The British symbol is as shown.

► Another widely used symbol for a NOT gate is the Military and American symbol, as shown.

► The logic state of the input or inputs and the output of a logic gate is shown in a *truth table*. The inputs are lettered A, B, C and so on and the output S. This truth table for the NOT gate indicates that when the input A is 1 then the output S is 0 and vice versa.

► *Boolean equations* are used as a mathematical way of expressing the truth table. A bar is used to denote 'not', so that an input of $\overline{A}$, 'not A', means that when A is not a 1 then the output will be a 1. The Boolean equation is $S = \overline{A}$.

EXERCISES

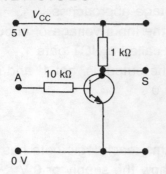

► Build the circuit shown in the diagram.

Connect A to V_{CC} and measure the base voltage. Note the logic state of A.

Measure the collector voltage. Note the logic state of the collector.

Connect A to 0 V and measure the base voltage. Note the logic state of A.

Measure the collector voltage and note its logic state.

From your results, state the type of logic gate, construct a truth table and write down a Boolean equation.

Fill in the missing words (1).
A logic 1 is a voltage in excess of _____ and a voltage of below about 0.4 V is termed a _____. For a NOT gate, when the input is a logic 1, the output will be _____. This gate is called a NOT gate because if the input is _____ the output is not _____.

. . . .

OR gates

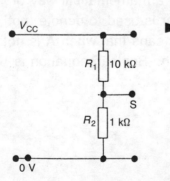

► The OR gate circuit uses a voltage divider to set the output voltage at S. The two resistors are chosen to give a logic 0 at the output.

For the circuit shown, when V_{CC} is 5 V, the output voltage is:

$$5 \text{ (V)} \times 1000 \text{ }(\Omega)/11\ 000 \text{ }(\Omega)$$

that is, about 0.45 V. This is logic 0.

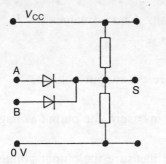

► An OR gate has two or more inputs. The gate shown in the diagram has two inputs, A and B. Each input has a diode with its cathode connected to the output.

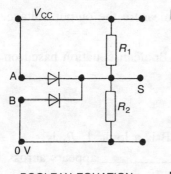

► If either diode A, or B, or both A and B are connected to V_{CC} the resistor R_1 will be shunted by the forward-biased diode allowing the voltage across R_2 to rise to a logic 1.

When either A or B is connected to 0 V, it will be reversed biased across R_2, so as not to affect the resistance of R_2 noticeably.

BOOLEAN EQUATION
$$S = A + B$$

► This gate is called the OR gate because if A or B inputs are logic 1 then the output will be logic 1.

The plus sign in the Boolean equation indicates an OR function.

TRUTH TABLE

A	B	S
0	0	0
1	0	1
0	1	1
1	1	1

► The truth table shown is for an OR gate. With a logic 1 on A, B, or A and B, the output is logic 1. Only when both A and B are at logic 0 is the output at logic 0.

BRITISH SYMBOL

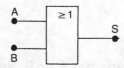

► The British symbol does not have a circle at the output, so the gate is not an inverting one. The '≥1' in the box is used to indicate that the gate is an OR gate.

AMERICAN SYMBOL

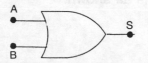

► For ease of drawing, all the British symbols have the same rectangular shape. The American symbols are all different shapes so that a 1 in the symbol is not necessary as the shape defines the function.

EXERCISES

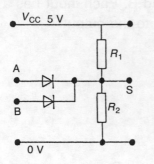

V_{CC} 5 V

R_1

A

S

B

R_2

0 V

▶ Build the circuit shown in the diagram. Choose values for R_1 and R_2 so that S = logic 0.

Connect A and B to 0 V and measure the output voltage.

Connect A to V_{CC} and B to 0 V and measure the output voltage.

Connect B to V_{CC} and A to 0 V and measure the output voltage.

Connect both A and B to V_{CC} and measure the output voltage.

Construct a truth table and write a Boolean equation based on the results.

Fill in the missing words (2).
If, in a NOR gate, A _____ B is a logic 1, R_1 is _____ circuited and a logic _____ appears across R_2. If neither A _____ B are at logic _____, the _____ divider consisting of R_1 and R_2 gives a logic _____ at S.

NOR gates

TRUTH TABLE		
A	B	S
0	0	1
0	1	0
1	0	0
1	1	0

BOOLEAN EQUATION
$S = \overline{A + B}$

▶ The truth table for the output of a NOR gate is exactly the opposite to that of the OR gate. Only when all the inputs are logic 0 will a logic 1 appear at the output.

▶ The Boolean expressions $\overline{A + B}$ means not A or B, so if A, or B, or A and B are logic 1, then the output S will not be logic 1. The Boolean equation is as shown.

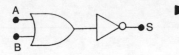

► Since the NOT gate is an inverter, the NOR function can be produced by inverting the output of an OR gate.

AMERICAN SYMBOL

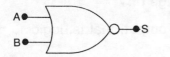

► The NOR gate symbol can be reduced to this. The circle at the output denotes an inverter and the symbol is that of an OR so that an inverted OR must be a NOT OR or NOR for short.

BRITISH SYMBOL

► The British symbol shows an OR gate with an inverting circle at the output.

· ·

EXERCISES

NOT

► Build the circuit shown in the diagram. Choose values of R_1 and R_2 so that S = logic 1.

Connect A and B to 0 V and measure the output voltage.

Next, measure the voltage at S with A connected to V_{CC}.

Connect both A and B to V_{CC} and measure the output voltage.

Construct a truth table and write a Boolean equation based on the results.

Fill in the missing words (3).
A NOR function can be obtained by using an _____ gate followed by a _____ gate. Only when both A and B are at logic _____ will the output be at logic _____.

· ·

AND gates

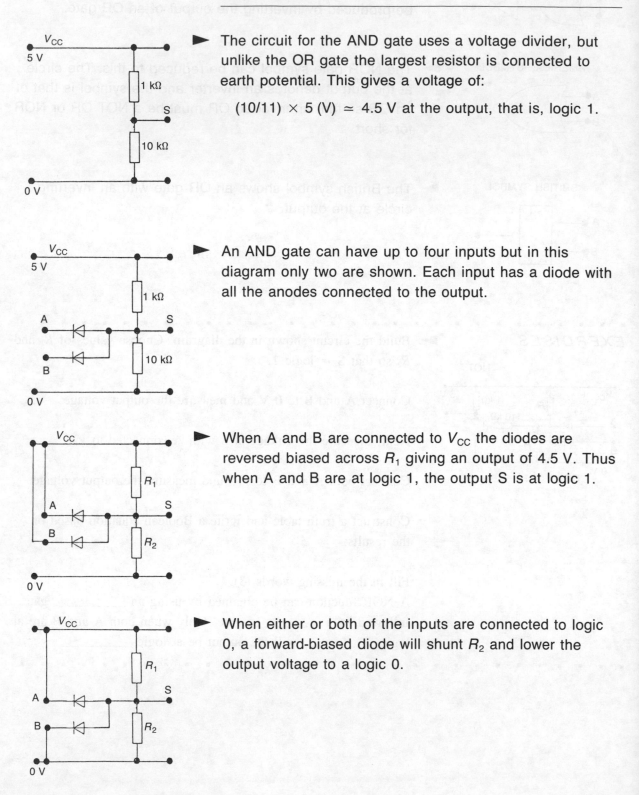

▶ The circuit for the AND gate uses a voltage divider, but unlike the OR gate the largest resistor is connected to earth potential. This gives a voltage of:

(10/11) × 5 (V) ≃ 4.5 V at the output, that is, logic 1.

▶ An AND gate can have up to four inputs but in this diagram only two are shown. Each input has a diode with all the anodes connected to the output.

▶ When A and B are connected to V_{CC} the diodes are reversed biased across R_1 giving an output of 4.5 V. Thus when A and B are at logic 1, the output S is at logic 1.

▶ When either or both of the inputs are connected to logic 0, a forward-biased diode will shunt R_2 and lower the output voltage to a logic 0.

TRUTH TABLE

A	B	S
0	0	0
0	1	0
1	0	0
1	1	1

► The truth table for an AND gate shows that only when both inputs are logic 1 will the output be logic 1.

BOOLEAN EQUATION
$S = AB$

► In Boolean algebra, the AND function is written as A.B or just AB and the Boolean equation for an AND function is as shown.

BRITISH SYMBOL

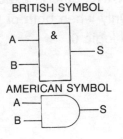

AMERICAN SYMBOL

► The symbols used when drawing circuit or logic diagrams are as shown.

- -

EXERCISES

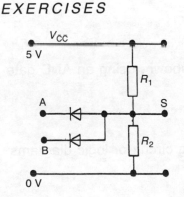

► Build the circuit shown in the diagram choosing values for R_1 and R_2 so that S is at logic 1.

Connect A and B to 0 V and measure the output voltage.

Measure the output voltage with A and then B connected to V_{CC}.

Connect both A and B to V_{CC} and measure the output voltage.

Write a Boolean equation and construct a truth table based on the results.

Fill in the missing words (4).

In a two-input AND gate, a logic 1 is produced at the output only when _____ and _____ are connected to _____. A logic 0 is produced at the output when _____ or _____ or _____ are connected to _____.

. . . .

NAND gates

TRUTH TABLE		
A	B	S
0	0	1
0	1	1
1	0	1
1	1	0

► The truth table for the output of a NAND gate is exactly opposite to that of the AND gate. Only when both of the inputs are logic 1 will the output be logic 0.

BOOLEAN EQUATION
$S = \overline{AB}$

► The Boolean expression for an AND function is AB. The Boolean expression for a NOT-AND or NAND function is $\overline{AB}$. Thus the Boolean equation for a NAND gate is as shown.

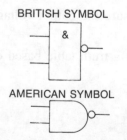

► A NAND gate can be made as shown, using an AND gate and a NOT gate.

BRITISH SYMBOL

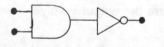

AMERICAN SYMBOL

► The symbols used when drawing circuit or logic diagrams are as shown.

EXERCISES

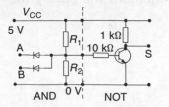

V_{CC}
5 V
A
B
R₁
R₂
1 kΩ
10 kΩ
S
0 V
AND   NOT

► Build the circuit shown in the diagram choosing values for R_1 and R_2 so that S is at logic 0.

Connect A and B to 0 V and measure the output voltage.

Connect A to V_{CC} and measure the output voltage.

Reverse the connections to the inputs of A and B and measure the output voltage.

Connect both A and B to V_{CC} and measure the output voltage.

Construct a truth table and write a Boolean equation based on the results.

Fill in the missing words (5).
A NAND gate is equivalent to an _____ gate followed by a _____ gate. A logic 0 output is only obtained when _____ and _____ are at logic _____.

Exclusive-NOR gates

TRUTH TABLE

A	B	S
0	0	1
0	1	0
1	0	0
1	1	1

► The truth table for the exclusive-NOR gate is as shown. As with the NOR gate if either A or B is a logic 1 the output is not a logic 1, but in an exclusive-NOR gate, if A and B are logic 1 then the output is logic 1.

BOOLEAN EQUATION
$S = AB + \overline{A}\overline{B}$

► From the truth table, it can be seen that an output of logic 1 is obtained both when A and B are logic 0 ($\overline{A}\overline{B}$) and also when A and B are logic 1, (AB). Thus the Boolean equation is as shown.

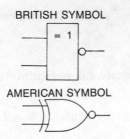

► The exclusive-NOR can be made up of three gates as shown in the diagram. This arrangement will satisfy the conditions of the truth table.

BRITISH SYMBOL

= 1

AMERICAN SYMBOL

► The symbols used when drawing circuit or logic diagrams are as shown.

. . . .

EXERCISES

► Build the circuit shown in the diagram choosing all the resistor values based on previous exercises.

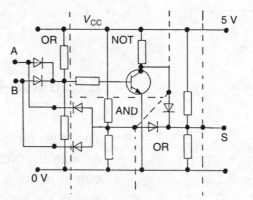

Connect A and B to 0 V and measure the output voltage.

Connect A to V_{CC} and measure the output voltage.

Reverse the connections to the inputs of A and B and measure the output voltage.

Connect both A and B to V_{CC} and measure the output voltage.

Write a Boolean equation and construct a truth table based on the results.

Fill in the missing words (6).
An exclusive-NOR gate gives a logic 1 output when A
_____ B are logic _____ and also when A
_____ B are logic _____.

- -

Exclusive-OR gates

TRUTH TABLE

A	B	S
0	0	0
0	1	1
1	0	1
1	1	0

► The truth table shown is for the exclusive-OR gate. The output is only a logic 1 if input A or B is a logic 1. When A and B are logic 1 then the output is logic 0.

BOOLEAN EQUATION
$S = \bar{A}B + A\bar{B}$

► From the truth table, a logic 1 output is obtained both when A is logic 0 and B is logic 1 ($\bar{A}B$) and also when A is logic 1 and B is logic 0 ($A\bar{B}$). Hence the Boolean equation is as shown.

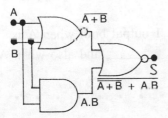

► An exclusive-OR function can be produced by inverting the exclusive-NOR function. The logic gate circuit to do this is as shown.

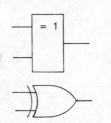

► The symbols used when drawing circuit or logic diagrams are as shown.

► Build the circuit shown in the diagram choosing all the resistor values based on previous exercises.

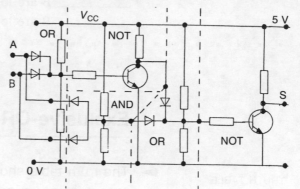

Connect A and B to 0 V and measure the output voltage.

Connect A to V_{CC} and measure the output voltage.

Reverse the input connections to A and B and measure the output voltage.

Connect A and B to V_{CC} and measure the output voltage.

Construct a truth table and write a Boolean equation based on the results.

Fill in the missing words (7).
An exclusive-OR gate gives a logic 1 output both when A is logic _____ and B is logic _____ and also when A is logic _____ and B is logic _____.

. . . .

Practical exercise:
a logic probe

Theory
A logic probe is used to detect whether a point in a circuit is at logic 0 or logic 1 level. Two lights are fitted, one known as the 'low light', equivalent to logic 0, and the other the 'high light', equivalent to logic 1. The logic probe consists essentially of three NOT gates.

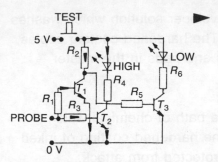

► When testing a point at logic 1 level, T_1 conducts (is on), causing T_3 not to conduct (be off). At the same time, T_2 is on, causing the high light to be on.

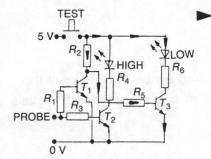

► When testing a point at logic 0 level, T_1 and T_2 are off, thus the high light is off. At the same time, a base current to T_3 via R_2 and R_5 turns T_3 on, causing the low light to be on.

► **Photosensitive boards**
In this practical exercise a printed-circuit board is produced using a photosensitive process. A *copper-clad board* can be purchased which has been sprayed or dipped into a light-sensitive solution. This coating must be kept in the dark, so it is covered with a dense black plastic covering which can be peeled off when a printed-circuit board is to be made.

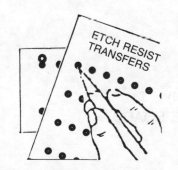

► A master positive of the printed-circuit board is made by positioning black rub-down transfers which will resist light penetration. A sticky-backed tape is used to form the tracks.

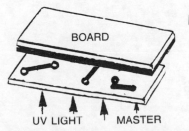

► The master positive is placed on top of a sensitive board after first removing the black plastic sheet and ultraviolet light is shone onto the board through the master film. Where the light touches the board the coating will be softened.

DEVELOPER

▶ The board is placed in a developer solution which washes away the softened coating. The hardened coating copies exactly the pattern of tracks and pads in the master positive design.

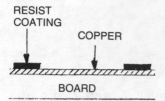

RESIST COATING

COPPER

BOARD

▶ The board is transferred to a bath of chemical which attacks copper, but where the hardened coating of inked resist exists the copper is protected from attack.

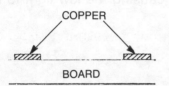

COPPER

BOARD

▶ The unprotected copper is etched away, leaving only the pattern of the tracks and pads in copper on the fibre-glass board.

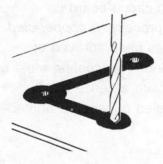

▶ The pads are drilled to take the component leads.

The advantage of using this method rather than an ink pen is that the master transparency can be kept and used again to produce as many identical printed-circuit boards as may be required.

Component list

3	BC183 L TRANSISTORS
3	1 kΩ RESISTORS
3	330 Ω RESISTORS
1	STANDARD LED (RED)
1	STANDARD LED (GREEN)
1	PIECE PHOTOSENSITIVE BOARD (45 mm × 28 mm)
1	RING TAG
2	3 mm NUTS
4	PILLARS
8	3 mm C/S SCREWS
4	CAPTIVE NUTS
4	SELF-TAPPING SCREWS
1	MOUNTING KIT BUSH

1	CORD GRIP BUSH
1	CROCODILE CLIP (BLACK)
1	CROCODILE CLIP (RED)
1	600 mm TWIN FLEX
1	MINIATURE PUSH BUTTON
1	35 mm SHRINK SLEEVING

Producing the PCB

► 1. Cut a piece of photographic board 45 mm × 28 mm.

2. Produce a full-size master diagram on transparent film.

3. Remove the protective layer and expose the board to ultraviolet light through the master.

4. Remove the light-sensitive coating.

5. Etch the copper from the board.

6. Drill the board and mount the components.

Assembling the logic probe

Cut the base from a material such as aluminium alloy and drill the holes while flat. The 4.8 mm fixing holes can be left. Fold tho base into shape.

Using a piece of $\frac{1}{8}$″ (3.175 mm) welding rod, use a die to cut a 3 mm thread on one end and grind the other to a point.

Fasten the probe to the base with a nut each side and insulate the probe from the base as it passes through the hole. Fit a ring tag to the probe.

Cut the lid from aluminium alloy and drill all the holes.

Fold the lid and place over the base. Mark the 4.8 mm fixing holes through the lid fixing holes and drill.

The lid can be painted if required.

CIRCUIT DIAGRAM

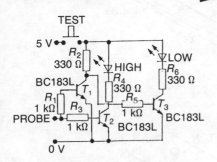

PCB LAYOUT

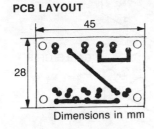

Dimensions in mm

COMPONENT LAYOUT

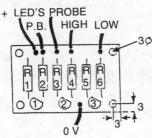

Dimensions in mm

LID AND BASE

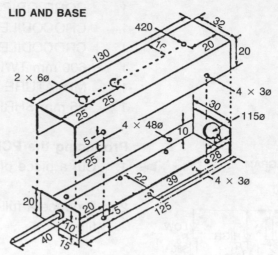

Dimensions in mm

ASSEMBLY

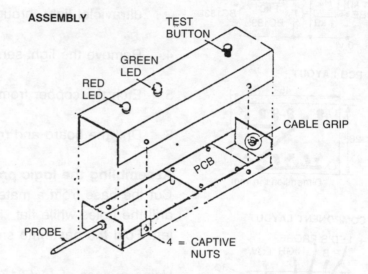

Fit the PCB into position using four 10 mm pillars.

A label can be fitted to the lid if required.

Fit two LEDs to the lid, the red one will indicate the high light and the green one the low light. Fit a test button to the lid.

Connect a red and a black insulated crocodile clip to 300 mm of twin flexible cable. The cable can be fed through a cable grip in the back of the base.

Connect all the components as shown in the circuit diagram.

Add No 4 captive nuts to the fixing holes and fasten the lid with No 4 self-tapping screws.

Self-assessment questions

1. DTL means:
   (a) diode transistor logic;
   (b) data transistor logic;
   (c) data triggered logic;
   (d) diode triggered logic.

2. A logic zero is:
   (a) always zero;
   (b) between 0 V and 0.4 V;
   (c) between 0.4 V and 0.7 V;
   (d) over 0.7 V.

3. A simple transistor circuit inverts making it a:
   (a) NOR gate;
   (b) OR gate;
   (c) NOT gate;
   (d) AND gate.

4. The Boolean equation $S = A + B$ is that of a:
   (a) NAND gate;
   (b) OR gate;
   (c) NOR gate;
   (d) AND gate.

5. To turn an OR gate into a NOR gate we must add a:
   (a) AND gate;
   (b) NAND gate;
   (c) NOT gate;
   (d) a second OR gate.

6. The AND gate has the expression:
   (a) $S = A + B$;
   (b) $S = \bar{A}$;
   (c) $S = AB$;
   (d) $S = \overline{AB}$.

7. A NOT added to an AND will give a:
   (a) NOR;
   (b) NAND;
   (c) OR;
   (d) AND.

8. A NOT added to a NAND will give a:
   (a) NOR;
   (b) NAND;
   (c) OR;
   (d) AND.

9. An exclusive-OR gate will give a logic 1 output if:
   (a) all the inputs are logic 1;
   (b) any of the inputs are logic 1;
   (c) both of these;
   (d) neither of these.

10. A logic 1 is:
   (a) over 0.7 V;
   (b) always 5 V;
   (c) never 5 V;
   (d) between 0 V and 0.4 V.

Answers to self-assessment questions
1. (a); 2. (b); 3. (c); 4. (b); 5. (c); 6. (c); 7. (b); 8. (d); 9. (b);
10. (a).

Missing words
(1) 0.7 V logic 0, logic 0, logic 1, not logic 1.
(2) OR, short, 1, NOR, 1, voltage, 0.
(3) OR, NOT, 0, 1.
(4) A, B, logic 1, A, B, A and B, 0 V.
(5) AND, NOT, A, B, 1.
(6) AND, 0, AND, 1.
(7) 0, 1, 1, 0.

Part 2
Multivibrators

BISTABLE OR FLIP FLOP CIRCUITS

. . . .

The R−S bistable

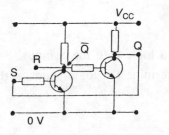

▶ The circuit shown is that of a *bistable multivibrator* sometimes called a *flip flop*. This particular flip flop is the R−S flip flop meaning the reset/set flip flop.

It can be seen that it is constructed from two NOT gates. The output of the first gate feeds the input of the second and the output of the second gate feeds back to the 'set' input of the first gate.

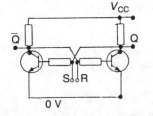

▶ It is more common to see this circuit drawn as shown in the diagram. Although the components are in different positions, it is exactly the same as the circuit shown above.

The Q at the output means the *quiescent* point or positive output and $\overline{Q}$ means the opposite of Q or NOT Q.

TRUTH TABLE			
R	S	Q	$\overline{Q}$
1	0	0	1
0	1	1	0
0	0	No change	
1	1	Indeterminate	

▶ When a logic 1 is applied at S, (the set input), Q either changes to or remains at logic 1. When a logic 1 is applied to R, (the reset input), Q either changes to or remains at logic 0. The Q output does not change when R and S = 0 and is indeterminate when R and S = 1.

► Assemble the circuit shown in the diagram.

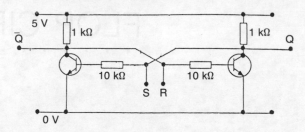

Apply a logic 1 to the S input and logic 0 to the R input. Measure the voltages and hence determine the logic states at the Q and $\bar{Q}$ outputs.

Apply a logic 1 to the R input and a logic 0 to the S input. Measure the voltages and hence determine the logic states at the Q and $\bar{Q}$ outputs.

Fill in the missing words (1).
The S input _____ the Q output to logic _____ and the $\bar{Q}$ output to logic _____.
The R input _____ the Q output to logic _____ and the $\bar{Q}$ output to logic _____.

Monostable multivibrators

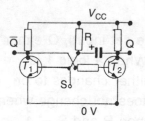

► Another multivibrator is the *monostable* type, sometimes referred to as a *timer*. It is called a monostable because it only has one stable position. When a logic 0 is applied to the set input, T_1 switches off and $\bar{Q}$ is logic 1. This means that the base of T_2 is logic 1, switching on T_2 and resetting the Q output to logic 0.

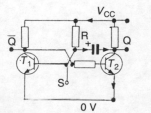

► When a logic 1 is applied to the set input, the capacitor charges via resistor R and T_2. When sufficiently charged, the left-hand plate of the capacitor is logic 1, applying a logic 1 to the base of T_1 which switches it on, making the $\bar{Q}$ output logic 0 and the Q output logic 1.

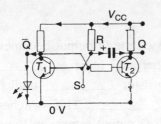

► These devices are used for creating time delays. If the capacitor has a large capacitance value, the time delay is long. Alternatively, if it has a small value, the time delay is short.

An indicator may be used to show when the timer is in operation.

TRUTH TABLE		
S	Q	$\bar{Q}$
0	0	1
1	1	0
	(after time delay)	

► The truth table shows that when S is set to logic 1, Q eventually switches to logic 1, and $\bar{Q}$ eventually switches to logic 0.

EXERCISES

► Assemble the circuit shown using a 100 μF capacitor.

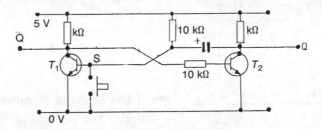

Press the set button, setting S to logic 0. Determine the logic states of Q and $\bar{Q}$.

Release the button. Measure the rise in voltage at the base of T_1.

Determine the logic states of Q and $\bar{Q}$.

Determine the time delay between releasing the button and Q changing logic state.

Change the capacitor to 500 μF and determine the new time delay.

Fill in the missing words (2).

When the _____ button is pressed the Q output becomes logic _____ and the Q̄ output becomes logic _____. The capacitor charges up via the transistor _____ until the base of _____ becomes logic _____. This switches on the transistor _____ and the Q output returns to logic _____ and the Q̄ output to logic _____. The time taken will depend upon the _____ value of the capacitor.

. . . .

Adjustable timers

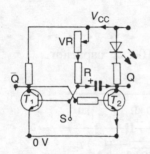

► It is possible to make the timer variable by using a variable resistor VR to alter the charging rate of the capacitor. A scale marked in seconds can be graduated around the knob to indicate the time interval.

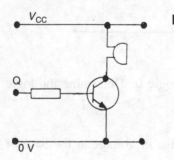

► If the timer is required to operate a bell, buzzer, siren or light, it is advisable to use a higher current transistor in the T_2 output stage, so as not to affect the operation of the timer. This is called a *buffer stage*.

. . . .

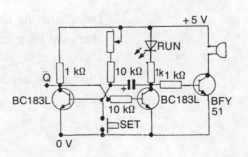

Build the timer shown in the diagram, choosing capacitance and variable resistance values to make an egg timer capable of timing 3 to 4 minutes.

Mark a graduated scale of time intervals.

Modify the diagram to switch off a mains lighting circuit after a time interval, using a relay and state a useful application.

Fill in the missing words (3).
Devices such as bells, buzzers and relays should be driven from a separate output stage called a _____ stage, so as not to upset the balance of the _____ circuit.

Astable multivibrators

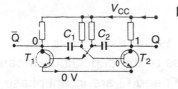

▶ The astable multivibrator has no stable state. When the supply is switched on, either T_1 or T_2 switches on. If T_1 switches on, base current flows via the base resistor causing collector current to flow and resetting the $\overline{Q}$ output to logic 0. This logic 0 is fed to the base of T_2 via capacitor C_1, holding it in the off position and making the Q output logic 1.

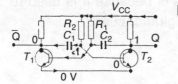

▶ As T_1 is switched on, there is a current path through R_2 and C_1 (which passes current when it is discharged) and down to earth potential via the collector/emitter junction or transistor T_1. This charges C_1 and its right-hand plate rises gradually to logic 1.

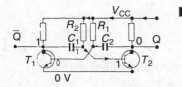

▶ When it reaches logic 1, the base of T_2 also becomes logic 1, switching on T_2 and making the Q output logic 0. This logic 0 is transferred via C_2 to the base of T_1, switching it off and making the $\overline{Q}$ output logic 1.

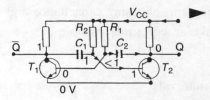

► Capacitor C_2 now has a charging path via R_1 and the collector/emitter junction of T_2 and its left-hand plate gradually rises to logic 1, which switches on T_1 again. The process repeats constantly. The frequency of the oscillations is dependent on the capacitance value of the capacitors.

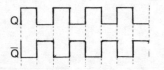

TRUTH TABLE	
Q	Q̄
0	1
1	0

► The astable multivibrator has no input as it is self-perpetuating. It can be seen from the truth table that the Q and Q̄ outputs are never the same as each other at the same moment in time.

► In theory the output waveforms viewed on an oscilloscope should be square rising from logic 0 to logic 1 instantly, staying at logic 1 level for a time period and falling back to logic 0 instantly.

► In practice this is not the case, as the rise time is not instant due to the charging times of the capacitors. It can be seen from the diagram that Q and Q̄ are in antiphase with each other.

► The astable is quite often referred to as a *clock*, and its waveform as a *clock pulse*. This is because it is used to synchronise changes in other digital circuits.

■ ■

EXERCISES

► Build the circuit shown in the diagram and connect the oscilloscope between the Q output and earth.

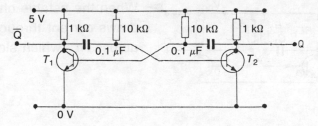

Draw the trace to scale as seen on the oscilloscope.

Determine the voltage level of the logic 1 level of the trace.
Determine the voltage level of the logic 0 level of the trace.

Using a dual-beam oscilloscope check the Q and Q̄ outputs at the same time.

Draw traces to scale as seen on the oscilloscope of the Q and Q̄ outputs.

Fill in the missing words (4).
If T_2 is the first transistor to switch on, its output Q becomes logic _____ and the base of T_1 becomes logic _____ making Q̄ logic _____. Capacitor _____ charges gradually through the collector/emitter of transistor _____. When it is charged, a logic 1 is applied to the _____ of _____, changing its state and the Q̄ output to logic _____. Capacitor _____ now charges through transistor _____ and a logic _____ is applied to the _____ of transistor _____, changing the _____ output to logic _____.

Astable multivibrators with waveform correction

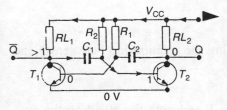

The reason that the output of the astable multivibrator is not a square wave is because if T_1 is the transistor to be switched off, the capacitor C_1 is drawing current through RL_1 to supply the base of T_2. This causes a voltage drop across RL_1 which holds the voltage at Q̄ low until C_1 is sufficiently charged.

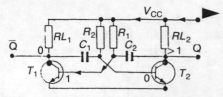

▶ When the astable changes state, T_1 switches on and draws current through C_2 and RL_2, causing a voltage drop across RL_2 which slows down the rise time of Q.

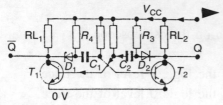

▶ When a reverse biased diode D_2 is added, current cannot flow through RL_2 and Q rises immediately, but C_2 has to be charged, so an extra load resistor R_3 is added to create a current path through C_2. Although charging C_2 is still delayed, this does not appear at the output.

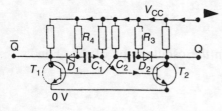

▶ When the astable changes its state, T_2 switches on and charges C_1 via resistor R_4. The diode D_1 allows $\overline{Q}$ to rise instantly and the output wave is square.

EXERCISES

▶ Build the circuit shown and display the Q and $\overline{Q}$ outputs on a twin beam oscilloscope.

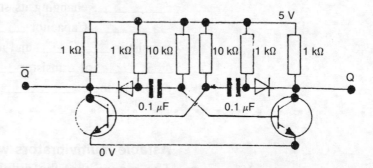

Draw the trace to scale, showing the relationship between Q and $\overline{Q}$.

Change the capacitors to 0.01 μF and note the effect on the frequency.

Fill in the missing words (5).

The waveforms at Q and $\bar{Q}$ become _____ because the _____ block the flow of current through the _____ resistors. When the transistors are switched, the Q and $\bar{Q}$ outputs _____ immediately but the _____ still need to charge, so extra _____ are added to form a _____ path.

●　●

Astable multivibrators with mark/space facilities

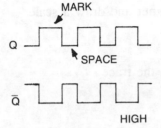

▶ Sometimes, due to the tolerance of resistors and capacitors in the circuit, the waveform is not square but rectangular.

If the Q output is logic 1 for a longer period than it is logic 0, then it is said to have a *high mark/space* ratio.

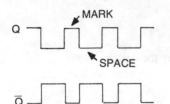

▶ If, on the other hand, the Q output is logic 0 for a longer period than it is logic 1, then it is said to have a *low mark/space* ratio.

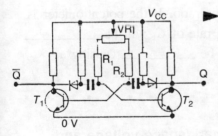

▶ The charging rate of the capacitors is set by the resistance values of R_1 and R_2, so that if one capacitor is charging faster than the other, that capacitor will need more series resistance to slow the charging rate down and the other less series resistance to speed the charging rate up. This can be achieved by adding a variable resistor VR_1.

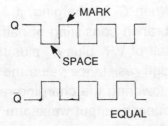

▶ With this control it is possible to set the mark/space ratio high, low or equal, as in the case of the square wave.

EXERCISES ▶ Build the circuit shown in the diagram and set the potentiometer to the far right.

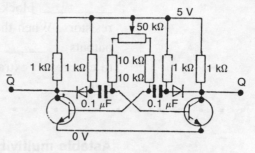

Connect the oscilloscope to the Q output and draw a scale drawing of the trace.

Determine the mark/space ratio from the trace.

Set the potentiometer to the far left.

Draw a scale drawing of the trace.

Determine the mark/space ratio from the trace.

Fill in the missing words (6)

If the potentiometer is set far to the left, the charging rate of C_1 is _____ and the charging rate of C_2 is _____ causing a _____ mark/space ratio. If the potentiometer is set far to the right, the charging rate of C_1 will be _____ and the charging rate of C_2 will be _____ causing a _____ mark/space ratio.

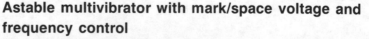

Astable multivibrator with mark/space voltage and frequency control

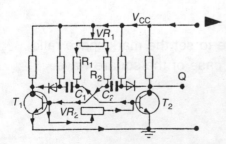

▶ To alter the frequency of the output wave form, a second variable resistor VR_2 is added. When C_1 is charging, it now charges through a parallel branch consisting of half of VR_1 plus R_1, in parallel with half of VR_1 plus R_2 plus the value of VR_2. If VR_2 is set to a high resistance value the equivalent resistance increases, lowering the charging rate of C_1 and producing a lower frequency output waveform. If VR_2 is set to a low resistance value, the opposite happens.

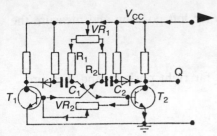

When C_2 is charging, the same parallel branch is in operation and the same portion of VR_2 is used, so that although the frequency of the output changes the mark/space ratio does not.

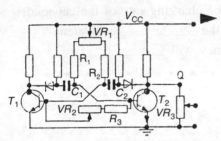

In practice, if VR_2 is set too low, the waveform collapses because the base of T_1 and the base of T_2 are effectively shorted together. A series resistor R_3 acts to prevent this happening.

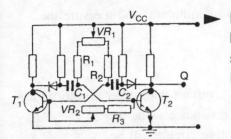

When the voltage of the waveform is too high, it can be reduced by adding another variable resistor VR_3 between the Q output and earth, using the wiper connection as the output. This divides the output voltage into whatever proportion is required.

EXERCISES

► Build the circuit shown in the diagram and connect the oscilloscope to the Q output.

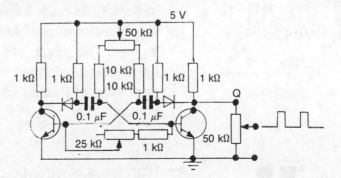

Set the output voltage to maximum volts. Set the mark/space ratio equal.

Set the frequency control to the far left position and measure the frequency of the Q output.

Set the frequency control to the far right position and measure the frequency of the Q output.

Measure the output voltage.

Turn the voltage level down to its minimum and measure the output voltage.

Fill in the missing words (7).

R_2 and VR_2 create a _____ circuit with other resistors VR_1 and R_1. If VR_2 is set at a high resistance value the _____ resistance of the capacitor charging circuit will be _____ and the frequency of the output waveform will _____.

If the value of VR_2 is reduced the charging rate of the capacitors will be _____ because of the _____ equivalent resistance and the output frequency will _____.

Other uses of astable multivibrators

Visual alarm

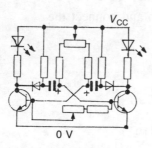

► An astable multivibrator has uses other than providing a clock pulse. One of these uses is to provide a visual alarm indicator. As each transistor switches on in turn, LEDs in the collector circuits light, giving alternating flashing signals. The length of time each LED is switched on can be adjusted using the mark/space control and the frequency of flashes can be adjusted using the frequency control.

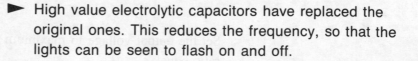

► High value electrolytic capacitors have replaced the original ones. This reduces the frequency, so that the lights can be seen to flash on and off.

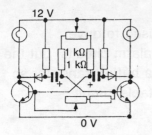

It is also possible to produce a flashing astable multivibrator using light bulbs, but the transistor base resistors must be reduced in value and the supply voltage adjusted to that required to light the bulbs. It may also be necessary to change the transistors to a higher current rating.

EXERCISES

► Build the circuit shown in the diagram and set the mark/space control to the far left. Note the effect on the LEDs.

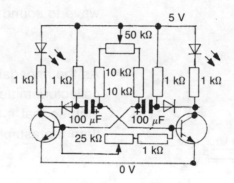

Move the mark/space control far to the right and note the effect on the LEDs.

Move the frequency control far to the right and note the effect on the LEDs.

Move the frequency control to the far left and note the effect on the LEDs.

Convert the circuit to a flashing bulb circuit.

Fill in the missing words (8).
The LEDs are _____ on at the same time because they are connected in the transistor _____ circuits. As the transistors switch on and off alternately, so the _____ turn on and off alternately.

Audible alarm

▶ Astable multivibrators can also be used to drive loudspeakers used, say, in audible alarm circuits, but the loudspeaker will need to be fed by a buffer transistor so as not to affect the action of the astable circuit.

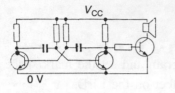

▶ The square waves produced at the Q output switches the buffer transistor on and off, producing an inverted square wave at the loudspeaker. This varying voltage will move the loudspeaker cone in and out, displacing the air in front of it and acting as a transducer, to convert the square wave to sound.

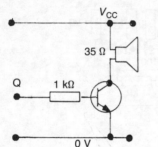

▶ As the impedance of the *loudspeaker* is relatively low, the collector/emitter current of the buffer transistor is relatively high so that it may need to have a higher current rating than the astable transistors.

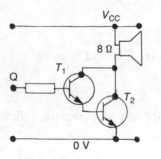

▶ Loudspeakers having a low impedance and a large sound output may reduce or stop the astable multivibrator Q output. An excellent buffer stage is a *Darlington pair* which will drive the loudspeaker without drawing large base currents from the Q output.

EXERCISES

▶ Build the circuit shown in the diagram.

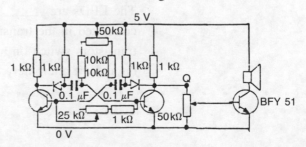

Change the capacitors to 0.01 μF and note the effect on the pitch of the sound.

Change the capacitors to 1.0 μF and note the effect on the pitch of the sound.

Fill in the missing words (9).
The astable multivibrator sends _____ wave pulses to the _____ of the buffer transistor, which produces pulses of current through the _____ to move the _____ and produce sound. Higher frequencies from the astable multivibrator produce a _____ pitched sound from the loudspeaker and lower frequencies will produce a _____ pitched sound from the loudspeaker. Changing the capacitor values will alter the _____.

Electronic keyboard

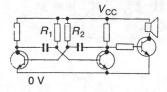

▶ The astable multivibrator is capable of creating sound and the pitch of the sound is dependent on the frequency of the Q output.

Changing the capacitance values alters the frequency but the frequency can also be changed by altering the values of R_1 and R_2, because the rate of charging the capacitors depends on these resistors.

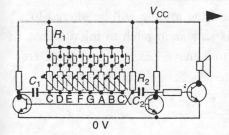

▶ If eight different resistance values are connected in series with R_1 via keys or push buttons, then the charging rate of C_1 can be varied eight times, to produce eight different sounds depending on which resistor is selected. If the series resistors are variable resistors, it is possible to tune these sounds to the eight notes in an octave, say, between middle C and top C.

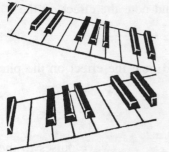

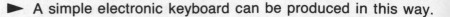

► A simple electronic keyboard can be produced in this way.

. . . .

EXERCISES   ► Assemble the circuit shown in the diagram.

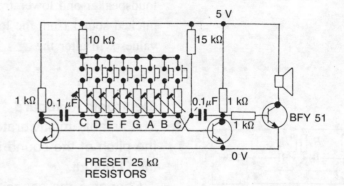

PRESET 25 kΩ
RESISTORS

Adjust the present resistors starting with C until a reasonable musical octave is achieved.

Fill in the missing words (10).

By adding the value of the C _____ to the value of the 10 kΩ resistor the _____ of the astable will be altered to produce a _____ which is similar in pitch to middle C. The other _____ are set to achieve _____ which are similar in pitch to the remaining _____ of an octave.

. . . .

Capacitance bridge

► An astable multivibrator can be used to drive a capacitance measuring bridge.

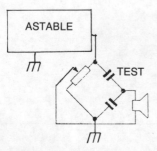

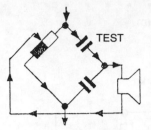

► When the current pulses reach the bridge, they have a choice of two current paths. The first is through the capacitor under test, through the loudspeaker, through the shaded part of the potentiometer and to earth.

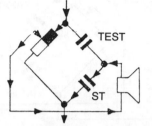

► The alternative path is through the other half of the potentiometer, through the loudspeaker in the opposite direction to that taken previously and through the internal standard capacitor (ST) to earth.

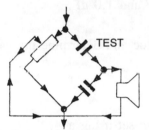

► Both of these currents will attempt to flow at the same time. The larger current is reduced by the amount of the smaller one and it follows then that the louder the sound from the loudspeaker, the more unbalanced the two circuits are.

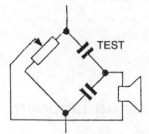

► The potentiometer is varied until the two currents are equal, when they will cancel each other and no sound is heard.

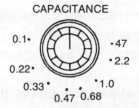

► A capacitance scale can be constructed using known values of test capacitors and marked around the potentiometer. When a quiet spot is found the value of the unknown capacitor can be read from this scale.

▶ Build the circuit shown in the diagram.

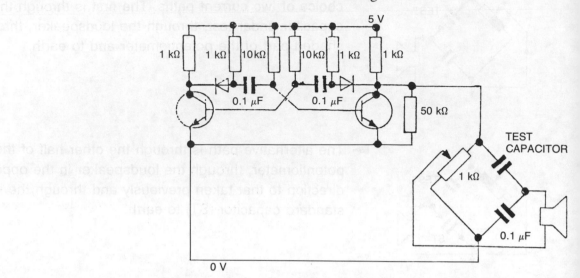

Make a paper scale of capacitance values by testing some known values of capacitors between 0.01 μF and 1.0 μF.

Test some capacitors of unknown value and determine the values using the paper scale.

Fill in the missing words (11).
The capacitance bridge balance can be set using a _____.
When balanced, the _____ remains silent because no _____ exists in the circuit. At this point, the _____ value can be read from the _____ scale.

Practical exercise:
a square wave generator using tagboard construction

Tagboard manufacture

▶ Tagboard is manufactured from resin-bonded paper with rows of solder tags along each edge. It is particularly useful for mounting axial components such as resistors and capacitors.

Before soldering components or wires to tagboard, the tag and the lead must be pre-tinned.

► A good strong mechanical joint is made by inserting the wire through the hole and bending the wire horizontally around the tag until it is completely encircled.

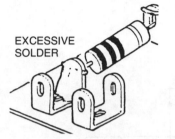

EXCESSIVE SOLDER

► A strong mechanical joint is made by the wrapping of the wire, soldering is used to make a good electrical connection. Feeding in too much solder serves no useful purpose and looks very untidy.

CORRECT SOLDER

► Feed in the solder until the joint is covered. Remove the solder first and then the soldering iron and allow the joint to cool naturally.

A good joint will be smooth, shiny, completely cover the joint and will have no solder spikes.

Parts list

4	1 kΩ RESISTORS
2	10 kΩ RESISTORS
2	0.1 μF CAPACITORS
2	BC 183L TRANSISTORS
2	IN 4001 DIODES
1	25 kΩ POTENTIOMETER
1	50 kΩ POTENTIOMETER
1	TAGBOARD GROUP PANEL (85 mm LONG)
2	4 mm SOCKETS (RED)
2	4 mm SOCKETS (BLACK)
4	CAPTIVE NUTS
8	No. 4 SELF-TAPPING SCREWS
4	RUBBER FEET
2	PLASTIC SPACERS
	PLASTIC BELT TIES
2	POTENTIOMETER KNOBS
2	YELLOW KNOB CAPS

CIRCUIT DIAGRAM

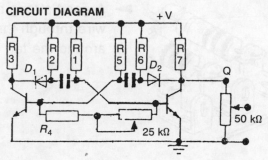

R_3, R_2, R_6, R_7, 1 kΩ
R_1, R_5, 10 kΩ
T_1, T_2, BC 183L
C_1, C_2, 0.1 μF

TAG BOARD LAYOUT

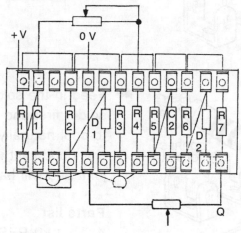

Component assembly on tagboard

1. Cut a piece of tagboard 85 mm long.
2. Solder the components to the board, except for D_2.
3. Solder the wires to the board and fasten in pairs using plastic belt ties.
4. Link wire all the relevant positions.
5. Add D_2 after fastening into the box.

The case

1. Cut the base from aluminium alloy or other suitable material and drill the holes while flat. The 4.8 mm fixing holes can be left.
2. Fold the base into shape.
3. Cut the lid from aluminium alloy and drill all the holes.

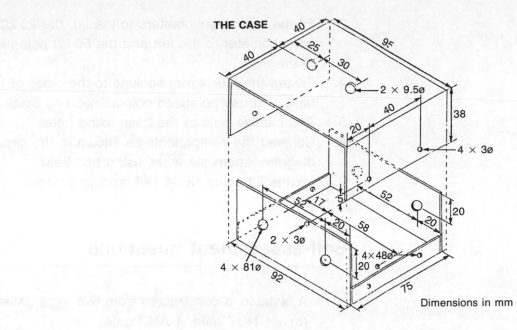

THE CASE

Dimensions in mm

4. Fold the lid and place over the base. Mark the
   4.8 mm fixing holes through the lid fixing holes and
   drill.
5. De-grease and paint as required.

Assembly

1. Fit the tagboard into position.
2. Manufacture a label for the box top.

ASSEMBLY

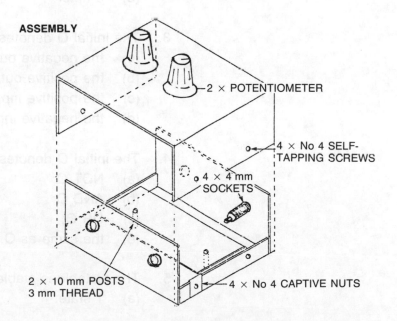

2 × POTENTIOMETER

4 × No 4 SELF-
TAPPING SCREWS

4 × 4 mm
SOCKETS

2 × 10 mm POSTS
3 mm THREAD

4 × No 4 CAPTIVE NUTS

3. Fit the two potentiometers to the lid, the 25 kΩ potentiometer to the left and the 50 kΩ potentiometer to the right.
4. Fasten the four 4 mm sockets to the sides of the base and use polarised colours red and black.
5. Add captive nuts to the base fixing holes.
6. Connect the components as shown in the circuit diagram. Loom the wires using belt ties.
7. Fix the lid using No. 4 self-tapping screws.

Self-assessment questions

1. A bistable is constructed from two logic gates:
   (a) 1 NOT gate, 1 AND gate;
   (b) 1 NOT gate, 1 NOR gate;
   (c) 2 NOT gates;
   (d) 2 AND gates.

2. Another name for the bistable is:
   (a) a clock;
   (b) a flip flop;
   (c) a flop flip;
   (d) a timer.

3. The initial Q denotes:
   (a) the negative output;
   (b) the positive output;
   (c) the positive input;
   (d) the negative input.

4. The initial $\overline{Q}$ denotes:
   (a) NOT Q;
   (b) AND Q;
   (c) OR Q;
   (d) the same as Q.

5. The bistable is stable in:
   (a) 1 state;

(b) 2 states;

(c) 3 states;

(d) no states.

6. The monostable has:

(a) 1 stable state;

(b) 2 stable states;

(c) 3 stable states;

(d) no stable states.

7. The monostable is used as a:

(a) flip flop;

(b) clock;

(c) timer;

(d) logic gate.

8. The length of time taken to reset the monostable is mainly governed by:

(a) The supply voltage;

(b) The value of base resistors;

(c) The capacitance values;

(d) The transistor gains.

9. The initial Q is the abbreviation of:

(a) quartz;

(b) quiescent;

(c) quantro;

(d) quarter.

10. The astable is stable in:

(a) 1 state;

(b) 2 states;

(c) 3 states;

(d) no states.

11. The astable is sometimes called:

(a) a clock;

(b) a timer;

(c) a watch;

(d) a flip flop.

12. The frequency of the astable depends on:
    (a) the value of the load resistors;
    (b) the gain of the transistors;
    (c) the value of the base resistors;
    (d) the value of the capacitors.

13. The output waveform of an astable should be:
    (a) a sine wave;
    (b) a triangular wave;
    (c) a square wave;
    (d) a sawtooth wave.

14. The output waveform is distorted unless we add:
    (a) blocking resistors;
    (b) blocking diodes;
    (c) blocking capacitors;
    (d) blocking transistors.

15. The ratio of the difference between the on time and the off time is called:
    (a) space mark;
    (b) mark space;
    (c) mark time;
    (d) time mark.

Answers to self-assessment questions

1. (c); 2. (b); 3. (b); 4. (a); 5. (b); 6. (a); 7. (c);
8. (c); 9. (b); 10. (d); 11. (a); 12. (d); 13. (c);
14. (b); 15. (b).

Missing words

(1) Sets, 1, 0, resets, 0, 1.
(2) Set, 0, 1, T_2, T_1, 1, T_1, 1, 0, capacitance.
(3) Buffer, timing.
(4) 0, 0, 1, C_2, T_2, base, T_1, 0, C_1, T_1, 1, base, T_2, Q, 0.
(5) Square, diodes, load, change, capacitors, resistors, current.
(6) Fast, slow, low, slow, fast, high.
(7) Parallel, equivalent, high, low, increased, lower, increase.
(8) Never, collector, LEDs.

(9)   Square, base, loudspeaker, cone, higher, lower, frequency.

(10)   Preset resistor, frequency, sound, preset resistors, sounds, notes.

(11)   Variable resistor, loudspeaker, current, capacitance, paper.

Part 3
Digital Microelectronics

INTEGRATED CIRCUIT LOGIC GATES

Quadruple, two-input NAND gates

► Logic gates are manufactured on chips of silicon and placed inside a plastic package, with pins down each side. This type of package is called a DIL package, which means the pins are Direct In Line. Wires within the package connect the silicon chip to the external pins. The package is called an *integrated circuit* (IC).

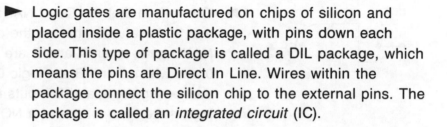

► All ICs are pin numbered in the same way, either a dot on the package denotes pin 1 or a notch is cut into the case between the first and the last pins.

With reference to the diagram shown, pins are numbered from left to right below the notch and back up the other side from right to left, the last pin being above the notch.

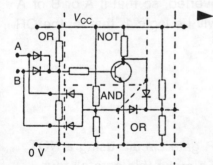

► Unlike the circuits so far built, using discrete diodes and transistors, called diode transistor logic (DTL), ICs use two different methods of construction, although the gates behave the same way.

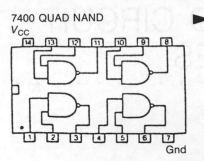

7400 QUAD NAND
V_{CC}
Gnd

► The first method is called transistor transistor logic (TTL). These ICs switch very fast from one logic state to another. They are usually prefixed by the number 74. The second two numbers, 00, in this case, indicate that the IC contains four, two-input NAND gates. This IC is probably the most common of all IC logic gates. They are designed to be used on a 5 V power supply and it can damage the IC if this voltage is greatly exceeded. Notice that the 0 V connection pin 7 is referred to as *ground* (Gnd).

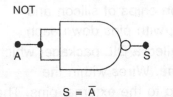

NOT
A
S

$S = \overline{A}$

► The reason that the Quad NAND gate is so common is that it is useful for making the other logic gates. For a NAND gate, when A and B are logic 1, the output is logic 0 and when A and B are logic 0, the output is logic 1. By connecting the A and B inputs together, only these two logic states can exist and a NOT gate results.

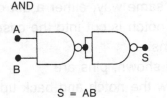

AND
A
B
S

$S = AB$

► An AND gate is obtained by adding a NOT gate to the output of a NAND gate, that is, by inverting the output of the NAND gate, as shown.

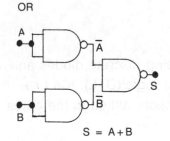

OR
A
$\overline{A}$
B
$\overline{B}$
S

$S = A + B$

► From the truth table of the NAND gate, if A, or B, or A and B is logic 0 the output will be logic 1. To make an OR gate both of the inputs are inverted, so that if A or B or A and B is logic 1, the output will be logic 1, that is, the OR function.

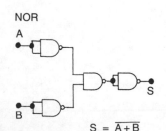

NOR
A
B
S

$S = \overline{A + B}$

► Inverting the output of the OR gate circuit, using a NOT gate produces a NOR gate. To make this gate all four gates in the IC have been used.

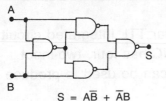

$$S = A\overline{B} + \overline{A}B$$

► By using all four gates, an exclusive-OR gate can be made. It can be shown, by using the rules and laws of Boolean algebra, that the output of the logic circuit shown gives an exclusive-OR function.

It is not possible to construct an exclusive-NOR from one Quad NAND gate, because another inverter is necessary at the output, making a total of five gates.

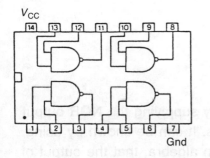

Gnd

► A very effective and simple way of determining the logic outputs of these gates is to connect a light-emitting diode (LED) between the output and ground. If the output is logic 1 the LED lights and conversely if it is logic 0, then it does not light. The input may be checked in the same way, as the LED draws only a very small current.

- -

EXERCISES

7400 QUADRUPLE
2-INPUT, NAND GATE

V_{CC}

Gnd

► Connect the IC as a NOT gate (note V_{CC} must not exceed 5 V).

Connect an LED at the output and prove the truth table.

Connect the IC as a NAND gate and prove the truth table.

Connect the IC as an AND gate and prove the truth table.

Connect the IC as a NOR gate and prove the truth table.

Connect the IC as an OR gate and prove the truth table.

Connect the IC as an exclusive-OR gate and prove the truth table.

Fill in the missing words (1).
It is possible to make all the logic gates from a 7400 Quad NAND IC except the _____ gate which needs _____ NAND gates. Any IC which starts with 74 must be a _____ logic gate and should not have a power supply which exceeds _____.

- -

Quadruple, two-input NOR gates

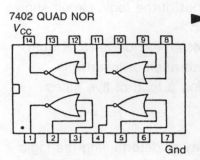

7402 QUAD NOR

► Probably the second most popular TTL integrated circuit is the 7402 Quad NOR gate. This IC has four, two-input NOR gates and like the 7400 it can be used to produce the other logic gates.

NOT

A   S

$S = \bar{A}$

► A NOR gate only gives a logic 1 output when both A and B inputs are logic 0. Thus, when A and B are connected together and to logic 0, the output is logic 1 and when A and B are logic 1 the output is logic 0. Thus the NOR gate becomes a NOT gate.

OR

A
    S
B

$S = A + B$

► An OR gate can be produced by inverting the output of the NOR gate, using a NOT gate. Thus, OR gates can be produced from one 7402 IC.

AND

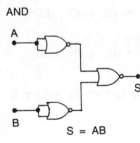

A

S

B

$S = AB$

► The AND gate is produced by supplying the NOR output gate via two NOT input gates. It can be shown by using the rules and laws of Boolean algebra, that the output of the logic circuit shown gives an AND function.

NAND

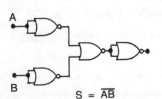

A

B $S = \overline{AB}$

► The AND gate can be converted to a NAND gate by the introduction of a NOT gate at the output of the AND gate, as shown.

EXCLUSIVE NOR

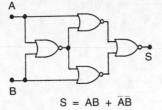

A

B

$$S = AB + \bar{A}\bar{B}$$

► It can be shown, by using the rules and laws of Boolean algebra, that the output of the logic circuit shown gives an exclusive-NOR function.

It is not possible to produce the exclusive-OR function, as an extra gate is needed to invert the output of the exclusive-NOR gate. However, it has been shown that the exclusive-OR function may be produced from the 7400 QUAD NAND IC.

► These two ICs, namely the 7400 and 7402, are very popular and very versatile but in some cases a little wasteful of gates. A range of TTL logic gates are produced, some of them less versatile and more specialised, but less wasteful of gates.

. . . .

EXERCISES

7402 QUADRUPLE
2-INPUT NOR GATE

V_{CC}

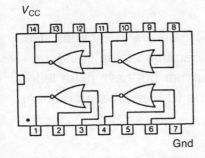

Gnd

► Connect the IC as a NOT gate (remember the supply volts must not exceed 5 V for TTL).

Connect an indicator to the output and prove the truth table.

Connect the IC as a NOR gate and prove the truth table.

Connect the IC as an OR gate and prove the truth table.

Connect the IC as a NAND gate and prove the truth table.

Connect the IC as an AND gate and prove the truth table.

Connect the IC as an exclusive-NOR gate and prove the truth table.

Fill in the missing words (2).
All the logic gates except the _____ gate can be made

from the 7402 Quad NOR gate. This, like the 7400, is a TTL gate which means _____, _____ logic.

• •

Special logic gates

QUAD SCHMITT NAND
74132

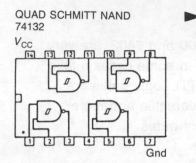

▶ An IC which operates primarily as a Quad NAND but has a special circuit construction is the *Schmitt gated* NAND. For a reliable operation TTL gates require fast input pulses because during the switch on and off periods they are vulnerable to noise and instability. A combined Quad NAND gate with Schmitt trigger facilities for shaping the input pulses is the 74132 gate.

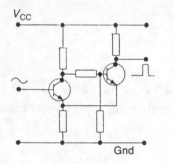

▶ The *Schmitt trigger* is an ideal circuit for interfacing slowly changing signals to logic circuits, as its output switches very fast and its input is capable of dealing with very slowly changing signals. It is even useful for changing sine waves to square waves.

74F132
74LS132
74ALS132

▶ Three further types of TTL logic gate are in common use. They have the same gate configuration as the standard TTL logic gates of the same number but have extra letters stamped between the 74 and the IC identification number.

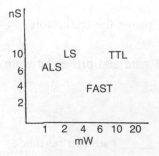

▶ LS means *low-power Schottky*; these ICs operate faster than standard TTL and use one-fifth of the power.
ALS means *advanced low-power Schottky* and operates at almost twice the speed of LS and with half of the power consumption.
F is the fastest switching IC but at the expense of increased power consumption over the LS and ALS ICs.

Complementary metal-oxide semiconductor logic gates

► Another type of logic gate is the complementary metal oxide semiconductor logic gate (CMOS). This type of gate does not use bipolar transistors but a special type of transistor called an IGFET (insulated gate field effect transistor).

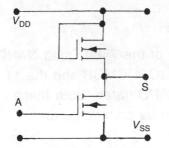

► CMOS transistors are not manufactured as single units, but are built in layers onto silicon chips for use in the 4000 B series integrated circuits. The connections are no longer referred to as base emitter and collector but as *gate, drain* and *source*.

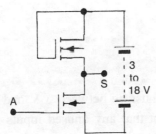

► They are called complementary because they do not work alone but in groups or pairs; the diagram shows a CMOS NOT gate. Notice that the supply rails are no longer termed V_{CC} and GND but V_{DD} and V_{SS}.

► The advantage of CMOS circuitry is that it is voltage controlled rather than current controlled as is TTL circuitry. Because the currents involved are extremely low they are ideal for battery-operated circuits, where battery life can be greatly extended. They also operate between voltages of 3 V and 18 V, unlike TTL which is limited to 5 V.

► The disadvantages of CMOS ICs are that they do not operate anything like as fast as TTL ICs and, because they are designed to operate on very minute currents, they are not designed to pass even moderate currents by TTL standards. Thus, even static electricity can damage them. For this reason they must not be handled unless special earthing precautions are taken.

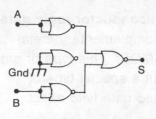

Static charges can also build up in the atmosphere and any unused inputs must not be left disconnected but must be connected to ground or the IC may be damaged.

CMOS ICs are transported in conductive foam which shorts all the pins together to reduce static charges. Full anti-static precautions must be observed when handling or soldering these components.

4001B QUAD NOR

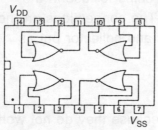

The CMOS version of the 7402 Quad NOR IC is the 4001B. The 40 prefix denotes the fact that the IC is CMOS and the 01 denotes that it contains four, two-input NOR gates. The input and output positions are different from those of the 7402 and so it must not be used as a direct replacement.

4011B QUAD NAND

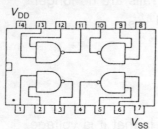

The 4011B is the CMOS version of the 7400 Quad NAND IC. Again the 40 means that the IC is CMOS and the 11 that it contains four, two-input NAND gates. Both these ICs are very widely used and can be connected to produce all the other logic gates.

- -

EXERCISES

4001B QUADRUPLE, 2-INPUT NOR GATE

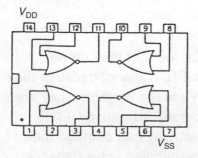

Connect the IC as a NOT gate. V_{DD} must be between 3 V and 18 V for CMOS gates. (It is important that any unused inputs are connected to 0 V.)

Connect an indicator to the output and prove the truth table.

Connect the IC as a NOR gate and prove the truth table.

Connect the IC as an OR gate and prove the truth table.

Connect the IC as a NAND gate and prove the truth table.

Connect the IC as an AND gate and prove the truth table.

Connect the IC as an exclusive-NOR gate and prove the truth table.

Fill in the missing words (3).
CMOS means _____ _____ _____
_____. CMOS ICs are easily damaged by _____
charges and must not be handled with fingers. To ensure
damage-free operation all _____ inputs must be grounded.

- -

- -

EXERCISES

4011B QUADRUPLE, 2-INPUT
NAND GATE

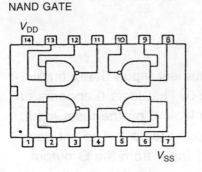

► Connect the IC as a NOT gate. Connect all unused inputs to
0 V.

Connect an indicator to the output and prove the truth table.

Connect the IC as a NAND gate and prove the truth table.

Connect the IC as an AND gate and prove the truth table.

Connect the IC as a NOR gate and prove the truth table.

Connect the IC as an OR gate and prove the truth table.

Connect the IC as an exclusive-OR gate and prove the truth
table.

Fill in the missing words (4).
The CMOS Quad NAND gate can be used to make all the other
logic gates except the _____ gate which can be made from
the _____ IC. An IC which begins with a 40 is always a
_____ gate.

INTEGRATED CIRCUIT MULTIVIBRATORS

· · · · · · · · · · · · · · · · · · ·

R–S bistable or flip flop

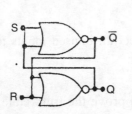

► A RESET–SET bistable can be produced by using two of the NOR gates manufactured into one of the popular integrated circuits such as the 7402 Quad NOR gate or the 4001B Quad NOR gate.

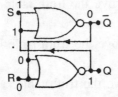

► When a logic 1 is applied to the set input, the Q̄ output is inverted and becomes a logic 0. That logic 0 appears on the reset gate together with a logic 0 on the reset input. Two logic 0s make the Q output a logic 1. The set gate now receives a second logic 1 input from the Q output enabling the set pulse to be released, with any change of state.

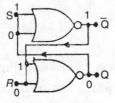

► When a logic 1 is applied to the reset input it overrides the logic 0 already there and changes the Q output to logic 0. This passes to the set input and as the previous set input has reverted back to logic 0 when the set pulse was released, these two logic 0s change the Q̄ output to logic 1.

► The truth table for the R–S bistable is as shown.

TRUTH TABLE			
R	S	Q	Q̄
1	0	0	1
0	1	1	0
0	0	NO CHANGE	
1	1	INDETERMINATE	

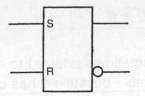

▶ The bistable only changes its state when the correct inputs are applied and in between signals, it remains stable, both when Q is 0 and Q is 1, hence the name bistable.

  The diagram shows the BS symbol for an R−S bistable. The circle denotes an inverted output making it the $\bar{Q}$ output.

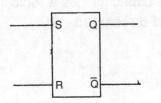

▶ Multivibrator symbols do not have to be oblong, a square is equally valid.

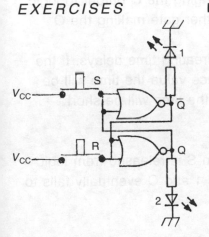

▶ The American version of the R−S bistable shows the Q and $\bar{Q}$ outputs rather than an inverting symbol at the $\bar{Q}$ output.

- -

EXERCISES

▶ Assemble the circuit shown.

Switch the set switch to logic 1 and note the effect on the LEDs.

Switch the reset switch to logic 1 and note the effect on the LEDs.

Repeat for all possible logic states on the set and reset switches and hence construct a truth table.

Fill in the missing words (5).

With a logic 1 on the set input, the $\bar{Q}$ output and the _____ input will be logic _____. This makes the Q output logic _____ and LED _____ is lit. When the reset is pressed the reset input will be logic _____ and the Q output will be logic _____. LED _____ is lit.

TRUTH TABLE			
R	S	Q	$\bar{Q}^+$

Monostable multivibrators

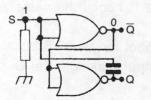

▶ The monostable multivibrator is sometimes referred to as the one shot. It is called a monostable because it has only one stable position.

The monostable can be made using a logic integrated circuit. If a logic 1 is applied to the set input both R and S inputs become logic 1, as they are connected together. The gate inverts the signal and the $\overline{Q}$ output becomes logic 0.

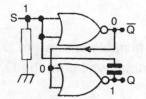

▶ This output appears at both the inputs of the second gate making the Q output logic 1. The capacitor has a logic 1 on both of its plates so it must be discharged.

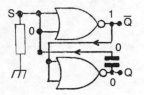

▶ When the set pulse is removed, the capacitor's charge changes until its top plate becomes logic 0. This overrides the logic 1 on the set gate changing the $\overline{Q}$ output to logic 1. This pulse appears on the other gate making the Q output 0.

These devices are used for creating time delays. If the capacitor has a large capacitance value the time will be long but if it has a small value the time will be short.

TRUTH TABLE		
S	Q	$\overline{Q}$
0	>0	<1
1	1	0

▶ The truth table shows that when S is released from logic 1, $\overline{Q}$ will eventually rise to logic 1 and Q eventually falls to logic 0.

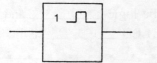

▶ The BS 3939 symbol is shown in the diagram. The single square pulse and the figure 1 show that this is a one shot or monostable. The absence of a circle at the output indicates the Q output.

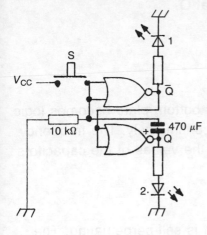

▶ Assemble the circuit shown in the diagram.

Press and release the set button, note which indicator is lit and how long it stays alight.

From the results, construct a truth table.

Devise and build a circuit to double the delay time of the monostable.

Fill in the missing words (6).
The monostable is used for creating a _____, it can be made from two _____ gates found in the _____ TTL IC or the _____ CMOS IC. When the set button is pressed the $\overline{Q}$ output will be inverted to logic _____ and LED _____ will _____. The capacitor charges gradually until the _____ input becomes logic _____ again switching _____ LED 1 and switching _____ LED 2.

Astable multivibrators

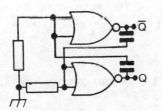

▶ The astable multivibrator or clock has no stable states. It can be made using two NOR gates. When the supply is switched onto the IC, one of the gates is the first to reach a logic 1 output state.

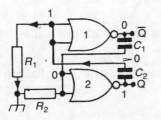

▶ Assume that gate 2 is this gate. If the inputs to gate 1 are logic 1, the $\overline{Q}$ output is logic 0. C_1 being uncharged has a logic 0 on both its plates, so gate 2 has two logic 0 inputs making the Q output logic 1. The top plate of C_2 gradually falls to logic 0 as C_2 charges via R_1 making gate 1 input logic 0.

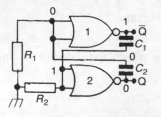

► This gives a logic 1 at $\bar{Q}$. The logic 1 at $\bar{Q}$ transfers to gate 2 input to give a logic 0 at Q.

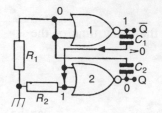

► C_1 now charges via R_2 until its bottom plate becomes logic 0 and the process will repeat continuously. The frequency of the oscillations depends on the values of the capacitors and the resistors.

TRUTH TABLE

Q	$\bar{Q}$
0	1
1	0

► The astable has no inputs as it is self-perpetuating. The truth table indicates that the Q and $\bar{Q}$ outputs are never the same as each other at the same moment in time.

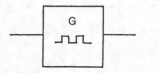

► The diagram shows the BS 3939 symbol for the astable. The G indicates that the unit is a generator and the double square pulse indicates that it is a continuous square wave generator.

EXERCISES

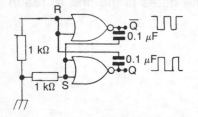

► Assemble the circuit shown.

Display the Q and $\bar{Q}$ outputs on the twin beam oscilloscope and note their phase relationship.

From the oscilloscope trace, estimate the frequency of the clock outputs.

Increase the clock frequency to ten times its original value.

Make one output remain at logic 1 level for ten times longer than the other.

Construct a truth table from the results.

Fill in the missing words (7).
If the Q output is logic 1 the S input is logic _____ and the $\overline{Q}$ output is logic _____. The Q capacitor charges until a logic _____ appears at the R input changing the $\overline{Q}$ output and the S input to logic _____. This process repeats itself producing a _____ wave at each output, provided the resistance and capacitance values are the _____.

Clocked R–S bistables

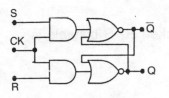

▶ Bistables are available in a wide variety of types, based on the R–S bistable. A clocked R–S bistable is produced by gating using two AND gates. The clocked R–S bistable only responds to a change in R and/or S when a clock pulse changes from logic 0 to logic 1 (*rising-edge triggered*), or in some cases, from logic 1 to logic 0 (*falling-edge triggered*).

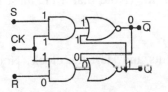

▶ If the S input has been set to logic 1 and the R input to logic 0, the next positive going clock pulse switches on the top AND gate allowing a logic 1 to pass to the input of the top NOR gate. The NOR gate gives a logic 0 at the $\overline{Q}$ output and a logic 0 at the bottom NOR gate input, to produce a logic 1 at the Q output.

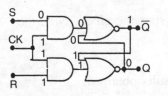

▶ Further clock pulses are ignored until a logic 1 is applied to the R input and a logic 0 to the S input. Then the bottom gate gives a logic 0 output at Q and a logic 1 output at $\overline{Q}$.

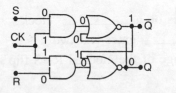

▶ When both S and R inputs are logic 0, the clock pulses do not cause a change in Q or $\overline{Q}$, since both AND gates retain their previous outputs. When both S and R inputs are at logic 1, the values of Q and $\overline{Q}$ are indeterminate.

S	R	Q
0	0	NO CHANGE
0	1	0
1	0	1
1	1	INDETERMINATE

▶ Changes in the Q output only occur when the clock pulses change from logic 0 to logic 1. The truth table is as shown.

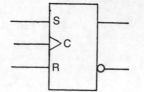

▶ The BS symbol for a rising-edge triggered bistable is shown.

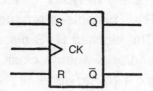

▶ The American symbol for a clocked R−S bistable is shown in the diagram.

. . . .

EXERCISES

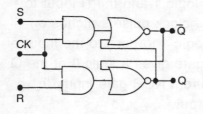

▶ Build the circuit shown in the diagram. (Note that TTL must not exceed 5 V supply.)

Apply a logic 0 to the S and R inputs and start the clock. Note the effect on the Q output.

Apply a logic 1 to the S input and start the clock. Note the effect on the Q output.

Reverse the inputs to S and R and start the clock. Note the effect on the Q output.

Construct a truth table from the results obtained.

Fill in the missing words (8).
The clocked R−S flip flop changes on a _____ clock pulse. It is made from two _____ gates and two _____ gates. The disadvantage of the clocked R−S flip

flop is that the outcome is _____ if two logic _____
are applied to the _____ and _____ inputs.

Preset and clear controls

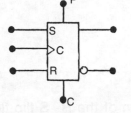

► Flip flops usually have two override controls. The first one is called the *preset* control. Connecting the preset input to V_{CC} presets the Q output to logic 1. The second control is the *clear* control. Connecting the clear input to V_{CC} sets the Q output to logic 0.

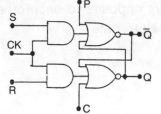

► The preset and clear connections are made to a third input on each NOR gate of the R−S latch and override any other inputs.

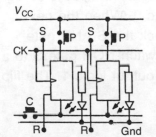

► A common clear control is useful when a number of bistables need to be set to zero simultaneously at the start of a process, while the preset controls can be used to set the Q outputs during a process.

EXERCISES

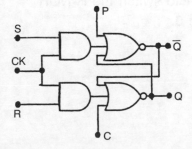

► Add the preset and clear connections to an R−S flip flop.

Set the Q output to logic 1 in the normal way using the S input.

Connect the clear input to logic 1 and note the effect on the Q output.

Connect the preset input to logic 1 and note the effect on the Q output.

Fill in the missing words (9).
The Q output can be set to logic 1 by connecting the
_____ input to logic _____. If the Q output has to
be returned to logic 0 the _____ input must be connected
to logic _____. Flip flops are set and reset individually
but can also be _____ or _____ simultaneously if
required.

D-type bistables

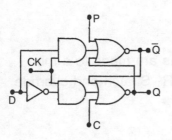

▶ The D-type flip flop is a modification of the R–S flip flop.
A NOT gate is connected in series with the reset input so
that the R and S inputs are always opposite to each other,
due to the inverting action of the NOT gate.

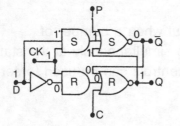

▶ If the D input is logic 1 then AND gate S input is at logic
1 and AND gate R input is at logic 0. When the next
positive pulse comes from the clock the S AND gate
switches giving a logic 1 output switch NOR gate S to a
logic 0 output. This makes the Q output logic 1. The flip
flop is now set.

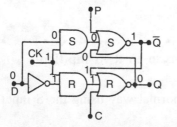

▶ To reset the Q output, a logic 0 is applied to the D input
and the NOT gate will invert it to supply a logic 1 to the R
AND gate. The AND gate will switch on with the next
clock pulse and supply a logic 1 to switch the R NOR
gate, making the Q output logic 0.

► Thus, the truth table is as shown. If D before the clock pulse is logic 0, after the clock pulse the Q output will always be logic 0 and if D is logic 1 before the clock pulse, then after the pulse Q will always be logic 1. That is, the Q output is always the same as the D input after a clock pulse.

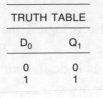

► The BS 3939 symbol for the D or Data flip flop is shown in the diagram. The absence of a circle at the clock input denotes a rising-edge triggered flip flop.

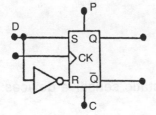

► The American version of the D flip flop is as shown.

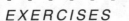

EXERCISES

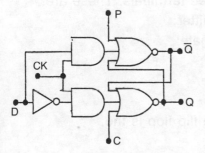

► Build the circuit shown in the diagram. (Note that TTL supplies must not exceed 5 V.)

Apply a logic 0 to the D input, preset the Q output and start the clock. Note the effect on the Q output.

Apply a logic 0 to the D input, clear the Q output and start the clock. Note the effect on the Q output.

Apply a logic 1 to the D input, preset the Q output and start the clock. Note the effect on the Q output.

Apply a logic 1 to the D input, clear the Q output and start the clock. Note the effect on the Q output.

Construct a truth table from the results.

Fill in the missing words (10).
If the D input before the _____ pulse is logic 1 the Q output after the _____ pulse is logic _____. But if the D input before the _____ pulse is logic 0, then after the _____ pulse the Q output will be logic _____.

• •

Self-assessment questions

1. TTL gates require a supply of:
   (a) 5 V;
   (b) 9 V;
   (c) 12 V;
   (d) 15 V.

2. Which of the following are static sensitive devices:
   (a) TTL;
   (b) bipolar;
   (c) discrete semiconductor;
   (d) CMOS.

3. A CMOS device has three terminals. These are:
   (a) base, collector, emitter;
   (b) collector, emitter, gate;
   (c) drain, source, gate;
   (d) drain, source, base.

4. The D input on a D-type flip flop is the:
   (a) delta input;
   (b) drain input;
   (c) data input;
   (d) dee input.

5. Pin one on an integrated circuit is marked with a:
   (a) cross;
   (b) spot;
   (c) star;
   (d) arrow.

6. TTL is the abbreviation of:
   (a) transistor timer logic;
   (b) timer transistor logic;
   (c) transistor transistor logic;
   (d) timer timer logic.

7. The lowest power consuming gates are:
   (a) LS;
   (b) ALS;
   (c) FAST;
   (d) TTL.

8. DIL is the abbreviation of:
   (a) direct in line;
   (b) drain in line;
   (c) data in line;
   (d) dot in line.

9. V_{CC} is the:
   (a) positive CMOS supply volts;
   (b) positive TTL supply volts;
   (c) negative CMOS supply volts;
   (d) negative TTL supply volts.

10. V_{DD} is the:
    (a) positive CMOS supply volts;
    (b) positive TTL supply volts;
    (c) negative CMOS supply volts;
    (d) negative TTL supply volts.

Answers to self-assessment questions
1. (a); 2. (d); 3. (c); 4. (c); 5. (b); 6. (c); 7. (b);
8. (a); 9. (b); 10. (a).

Missing words
(1) exclusive-NOR, five, TTL, 5 V.
(2) exclusive-OR, transistor, transistor.
(3) complementary metal oxide semiconductor, static, unused.
(4) exclusive-NOR, 4001 Quad NOR, CMOS.
(5) reset, 0, 1, 2, 1, 0, 1.

(6) time delay, NOR, 7402, 4001, 0, 2, light, set, 0, on, off.

(7) 0, 0, 0, 1, square, same.

(8) positive going, NOR, AND, uncertain, one's, R, S.

(9) preset, 1, clear, 1, preset, cleared.

(10) clock, clock, 1, clock, clock, 0.

Part 4
Shift Registers, Adders and Counters

SHIFT REGISTERS

. . . .

SISO D-type shift registers

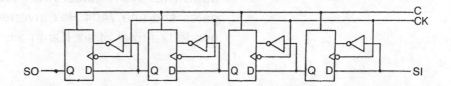

The diagram shows four D-type flip flops connected to form a serial input, serial output (SISO), shift register. If a logic 1 is applied to the serial input, the next clock pulse moves the logic 1 to the Q output of the first flip flop and therefore to the input of the second flip flop, to await the second clock pulse. This continues until after four pulses of the clock the logic 1 will appear at the output of the fourth flip flop. In this way, four bits of information can be stored in the form of logic 1's or logic 0's.

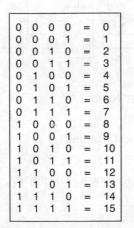

► All denary numbers have a corresponding binary code, made up of logic 1's and logic 0's, called *bits*. The four-bit shift register can store four such bits. The maximum number of combinations of ones or zeros for a 4-bit system is sixteen, so the register can store numbers 0 to 15. Higher numbers need larger shift registers containing more bits. Binary numbers are read from right to left in the register.

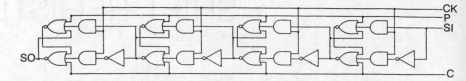

The circuit diagram shows the number of logic gates necessary to construct a four-bit SISO shift register. From the selection of logic gate integrated circuits available, three 7427 NOR gates, two 7408 quadruple two-input AND gates and one 7404 Hex inverter integrated circuits are needed, a total of six ICs in all.

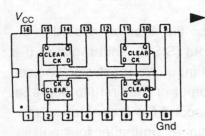

► A dedicated IC is available to simplify the construction of shift registers and counters.

    The 74145 Quad D-type flip flop is an ideal choice for constructing a shift register.

EXERCISES

Build the circuit shown in the diagram.

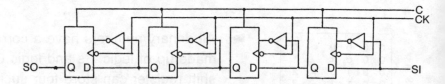

Clear the register and set the SI input at logic 1.

Apply one clock pulse and record all the Q outputs.

Remove the logic 1 serial input and apply one clock pulse.

Record the four-bit data at the Q outputs.

Set the serial input to logic 1 and apply two clock pulses.

Record the four-bit data at the Q outputs.

Fill in the missing words (1).

The serial input determines the logic information and the
_____ send the information through the register. A logic
_____ at the series input stores a logic 1 in the register
and a logic _____ stores a logic 0 in the register. A
denary number between 0 and _____ can be stored in a
_____ bit register.

. . . .

SIPO D-type shift registers

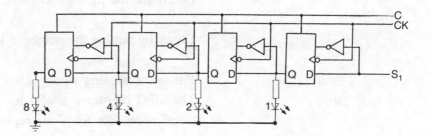

Another type of shift register is the serial input parallel
output, (SIPO) shift register. This shift register is not as
useful for moving serial information as the SISO register
and it has four output lines instead of one. It is, however,
extremely useful if all the data has to be read
instantaneously.

The LEDs connected at each output indicate the binary
information stored in the register. The flip flop nearest the
serial input gives the *least significant bit* output, that is,
the bit which adds least significantly to the numerical total.
Conversely, the flip flop furthest from the serial input gives
the *most significant bit*.

The output lines can be numbered 8, 4, 2 and 1 as shown
and from this a mental conversion to digital numbering
can be done. For example, if the 8 line is lit then the
number is 8. If the 8 line and the 2 line are lit, the number
is 8 + 2 = 10.

Build the circuit shown in the diagram and add LEDs to each output.

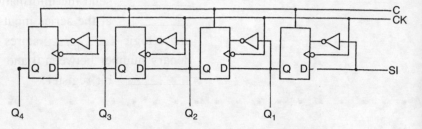

Clear the register and record the denary number 1 followed by the denary number 2, through to denary number 10.

Determine the light patterns for denary numbers 11 to 15.

Check by putting the numbers 11 to 15 into the register.

Fill in the missing words (2).
The SIPO register is useful for reading data _____. For transferring data from one register to another the _____ register is more useful as it only needs _____ output line/lines.

· ·

Binary to decimal decoders

The diagram shows a binary to decimal decoder. If the binary output from a parallel output register is fed into the bus lines marked 1, 2, 4 and 8, these lines are at a positive voltage when a logic 1 is stored in that particular part of the shift register. Four zero voltage lines can also be produced by inverting the original four lines using NOT gates. The shift register stores any number from 0 to 15, so sixteen output lines are needed to supply sixteen numbered LED indicators.

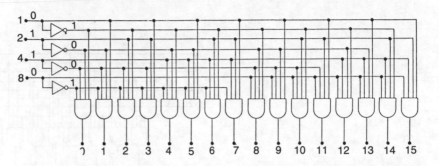

Assume the shift register is holding the denary number 6 in binary form. The binary code for 6 is 0110, which is fed into the bus lines. The inverted bus lines become 1001. By checking the diagram only gate 6 has four logic 1 signals at its inputs so that only gate 6 outputs a logic 1 and only LED 6 lights. The binary code for 6 has been converted to a decimal display for 6.

74154, 4 to 16 line Decoder

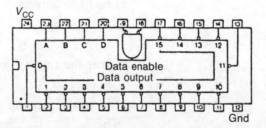

Dedicated decoders are manufactured. The 74154 four-input to sixteen-output line decoder is ideal for replacing the sixteen AND gates and four NOT gates that were used to make the decoder. It is very much cheaper to buy the one IC and also easier to use.

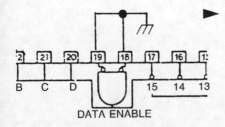

► Pins 18 and 19 of the 74154 IC are the inputs to a two-input NAND gate which enables the decoder to operate if either of these pins is connected to logic 0. If both inputs are logic 1, the decoder is temporarily disabled.

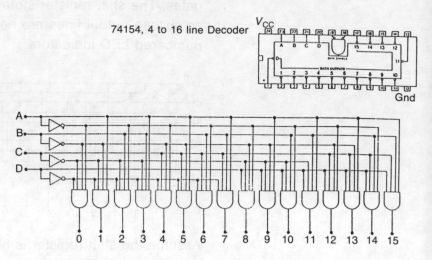

EXERCISES

Build the circuit shown in the diagram, using a 74154 IC.

74154, 4 to 16 line Decoder

A
B
C
D

0 1 2 3 4 5 6 7 8 9 10 11 12 13 14 15

Connect the decoder to an SIPO shift register. Add LEDs to the outputs.

Load the register via SI until light 5 appears. Determine the binary code for this light.

Load the register via SI with binary code 1110. Note which light appears.

Clear the register and note which light appears.

Fill in the missing words (3).
The _____ output from the _____ can be converted into _____ using a _____. The _____ is made mainly from _____ gates fed from _____ lines. All the _____ gate inputs must be logic _____ to light the relevant _____.

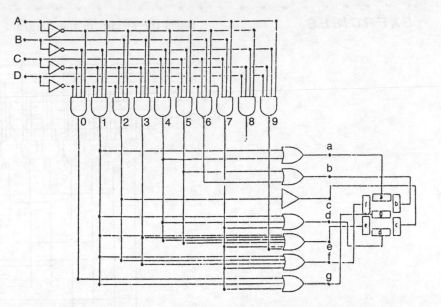

It is not possible to display to 15 in decimal unless two seven-segment displays are used. A single *seven-segment display* only displays from denary 0 to 9.

7448 BC-to-7 segment decoder/driver

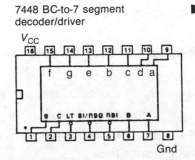

► A range of binary to *seven-segment decoder/drivers* exist. The diagram shows a 7448 decoder.

A logic 0 on lamp test (LT) lights all the LEDs for test purposes, so it is normal to connect pin 3 to logic 1. A logic 0 on blanking input will blank out all the LEDs so pin 4 should normally be logic 1. RBI and RBO are abbreviations for ripple blanking input and ripple blanking output. They too can be disabled by a logic 1 input at pins 4 and 5.

Build the circuit in the diagram using appropriate ICs.

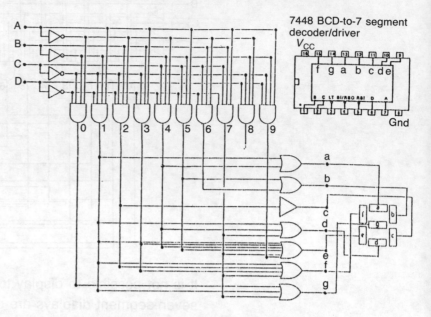

7448 BCD-to-7 segment decoder/driver

Test the circuit by setting up the binary code for 0 into the bus lines and noting the display.

Check each binary code in turn from denary 0 to 9.

Connect the bus lines to a SIPO shift register, enter the code to display 7.

Fill in the missing words (4).

A _____ segment display can display numbers from _____ to _____. Numbers greater than _____ require two or more _____.

PIPO shift registers

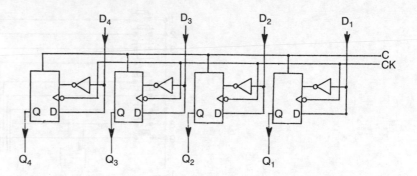

Another register is the parallel input parallel output (PIPO) shift register. Each D-type flip flop is loaded separately and often instantaneously using a four-bit binary code and emptied instantaneously on receipt of a common clock pulse.

EXERCISES

Build the circuit shown in the diagram, connecting D_1 to D_4 to an SIPO register.

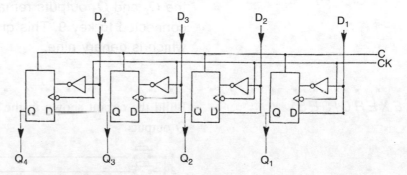

Connect the binary to decimal decoder and seven-segment display to the output lines, Q_1 to Q_4.

Enter all the binary codes from 0 to 9 and note the display.

Fill in the missing words (5).
The PIPO shift register is used to input a _____ bit _____ number on a single _____ and empty it at the output on a second _____.

Decimal to binary encoders

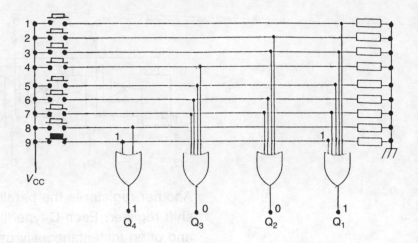

To change a decimal number from a keypad to a binary number, an encoder can be used. The encoder has four OR gates with each input held to logic 0 by resistors. If a key is selected, say, key 9, gates 1 and 4 receive logic 1s at their inputs producing a logic 1 at the Q outputs. The Q_1 and Q_4 outputs will consequently become logic 1s but the Q_2 and Q_3 outputs remain at logic 0, as they are not connected to key 9. This gives a binary code of 1001 which is denary nine.

EXERCISES

Build the circuit shown in the diagram and connect LEDs to the Q outputs.

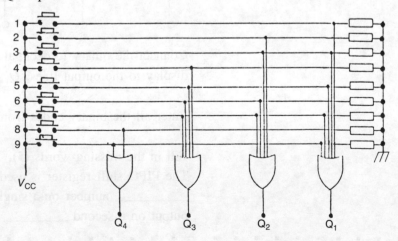

Press the keys 1 to 9 in turn and check the light pattern against the correct binary code.

By following the circuit diagram, predict the binary output if 5 is pressed.

Press 5 and check this prediction.

Fill in the missing words (6).
The decimal to binary encoder reduces the _____ line keypad output to a four-bit _____ code at the _____ outputs. The resistors in the diagram ensure that unused _____ are held at _____.

. . . .

An encoder with memory

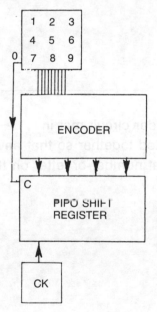

► Although the encoder converts the key value into binary code, as soon as the key is released the encoder reverts to binary 0.

If the encoder output is connected to a PIPO shift register, it remains stored until it is moved out by a clock pulse or until a different input key is pressed.

If the zero key is pressed, the encoder is not needed, as the key is connected directly to the clear input on the shift register.

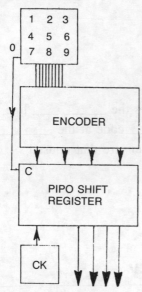

► Add a PIPO shift register to a decimal to binary encoder circuit and connect the key 0 line to the clear input of the register.

Connect LEDs to the output lines and press a key.

Apply a clock pulse to the shift register and note the output code.

Check all the denary key inputs against the binary number outputs.

Fill in the missing words (7).
The _____ alone will not store the _____ number, so a _____ can be used as a memory unit. The _____ can be emptied by a single _____ pulse.

An encoder/decoder

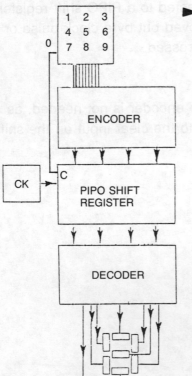

► The encoder circuit and the decoder circuit met in previous sections can be connected together so that any key can be pressed to display that number or letter on the seven-segment display.

EXERCISES

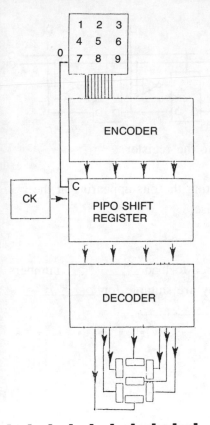

► Connect the circuit shown in the diagram.

Select each decimal number in turn, starting at 0.

Apply a pulse to clock the shift register between each number and note the output on the display.

Fill in the missing words (8).
The encoder changes the _____ input to a _____ code, which is passed to the _____ during a _____ pulse. It is _____ in the _____ until another _____ is applied. The decoder converts the _____ code into a _____ segment display code.

· ·

PISO shift registers

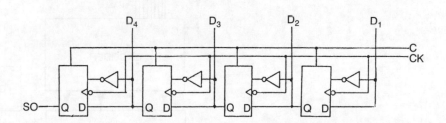

Another type of shift register is the parallel input, serial output (PISO) register. This register is loaded via push-buttons or a keyboard, each bistable having its own input. The serial output enables movement of bits to another location, one bit at a time, via only one line.

Build the circuit shown in the diagram.

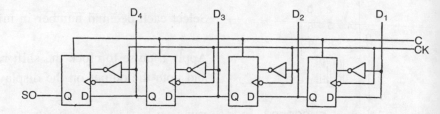

Enter the binary code for six into the register.

Clock the register four times noting the bits appearing at the serial output with each clock pulse.

Fill in the missing words (9).
Parallel input registers can be used to load _____ numbers during a single clock pulse. They are suitable for _____ loading of _____ from a _____.

Serial data transfer

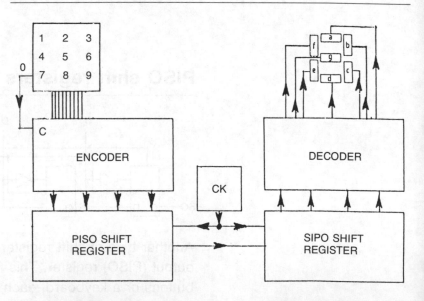

To reduce the number of tracks on a PCB and hence its size it is sometimes advantageous to transfer information serially as it requires only one data line. To do this two shift registers are required. The data is first loaded into a

PISO shift register on the first clock pulse and moved into the SIPO register on the next four clock pulses. From there it can be decoded in the usual way.

EXERCISES

Build the circuit shown in the diagram.

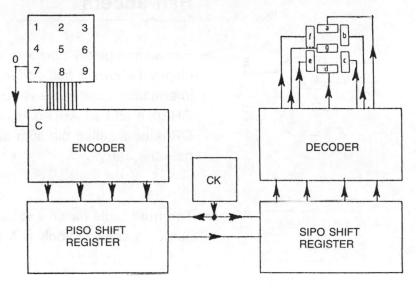

Select a number on the key pad.

Pulse the clock and check that the number is in the shift register.

Pulse the clock four times and check that the number on the display is the one you selected.

Fill in the missing words (10).

_____ movement of _____ can be useful in some circumstances because it reduces the number of data _____ needed in the circuit and hence the PCB _____ .

ADDER CIRCUITS
. . . .

Half adders

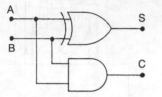

► Sometimes binary numbers must be added together. The diagram shows a *half adder*, which adds two bits of information together. It is constructed from an exclusive-OR gate and an AND gate. The output from the exclusive-OR gate is called the sum and the output from the AND gate the carry.

TRUTH TABLE		
A	B	S
0	0	0
0	1	1
1	0	1
1	1	0

► The truth table for an exclusive-OR gate is as shown. A 1 output is achieved only if A or B is logic 1.

TRUTH TABLE		
A	B	C
0	0	0
0	1	0
1	0	0
1	1	1

► The truth table for an AND gate is as shown. A logic 1 appears at the output only when both inputs are logic 1.

TRUTH TABLE			
A	B	S	C
0	0	0	0
0	1	1	0
1	0	1	0
1	1	0	1

► The truth table for a half adder is as shown. When either A or B is 1, there is a 1 output in the S column and when both A and B are 1, there is a 1 in the C column.

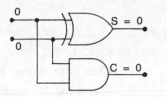

► When two binary 0s are added, the result is sum = 0, carry = 0, which complies with the half adder truth table.

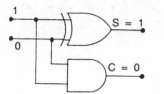

► The binary addition of 1 + 0 gives sum = 1, carry = 0, complying with the half adder truth table.

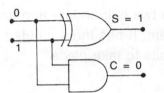

► The binary addition of 0 + 1 gives sum = 1, carry = 0, complying with the half adder truth table.

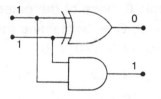

► The binary addition of 1 + 1 gives sum 0, carry 1 (since there is no 2 in a binary system) which again complies with the truth table for a half adder circuit. Thus all the requirements of the binary addition of two bits are met by a half adder circuit.

EXERCISES

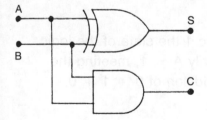

► Connect the circuit shown in the diagram.

Connect the S and C outputs to light-emitting diodes.

Connect both inputs to logic 0 and note the binary output.

Connect A to logic 1 and note the binary output.

Reverse the A and B connections and note the binary output.

Connect both inputs to logic 1 and note the binary output.

Fill in the missing words (11).

The half adder is constructed using an _____ gate and an
_____ gate. Only when A or B is at logic 1 will the
_____ output be logic _____. When both A and B
are logic 1 the S output is logic _____ and the C output is
logic _____.

• •

Full adders

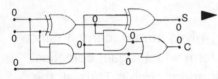

► A *full adder* is constructed from two half adders and an
OR gate as shown in the diagram. It has three inputs
enabling additions up to three bits to take place.

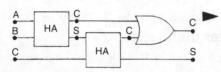

► The diagram shows the logic gate circuit diagram of the
full adder. If all the inputs are logic 0, none of the gates
has a logic 1 output, that is, S = 0, C = 0, meeting the
requirements of the binary addition of 0 + 0 + 0.

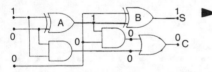

► When only the A input is at logic 1, both the output of
gate A and the input of gate B are logic 1, giving S = 1,
C = 0. This meets the requirement of the binary addition
of 1 + 0 + 0.

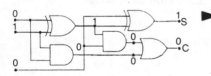

► When only the B input is logic 1 the state of the logic
gates is the same as when only A = 1, meeting the
requirements of the binary addition of 0 + 1 + 0.

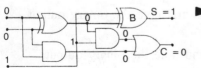

► When only the C input is logic 1 the state of the logic
gates is as shown. This meets the requirements of the
binary addition of 0 + 0 + 1, giving S = 1, C = 0.

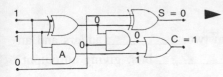

► In binary arithmetic, 1 + 1 + 0 gives sum = 0, carry = 1. It can be seen that the logic circuit shown achieves this.

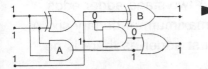

► In binary arithmetic, both 1 + 0 + 1 and 0 + 1 + 1 give sum = 0, carry = 1. It can be seen that the logic circuit shown achieves this, since a logic 1 on either the A or B input to the exclusive-OR gate gives a logic 1 at the output.

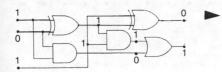

► In binary arithmetic, 1 + 1 + 1 gives sum = 1, carry = 1. It can be seen that the logic circuit shown achieves this. Thus the full adder logic circuit meets all the requirements of the addition of three bits.

► The diagram shows the truth table for a full adder.

INPUTS			OUTPUTS	
A	B	C	S	C
0	0	0	0	0
1	0	0	1	0
0	1	0	1	0
0	0	1	1	0
1	1	0	0	1
0	1	1	0	1
1	0	1	0	1
1	1	1	1	1

EXERCISES

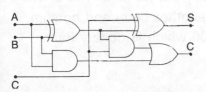

► Build the circuit shown in the diagram.

Connect light-emitting diodes to the S and C outputs.

Apply a logic 1 to each of the inputs in turn and note the S and C outputs.

Apply logic 1 first to A and B, then B and C and finally A and C and note the S and C outputs.

Apply logic 1 to the three inputs and note the S and C outputs.

Fill in the missing words (12).

A full adder is constructed from two _____ adders and an
_____ gate. It can add _____ bits, giving an output
as a _____ and a _____.

. . . .

Four-bit adders

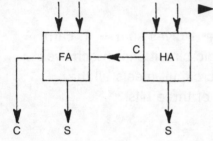

► Adders can be cascaded by taking the carry of one adder
to the third input of the next. A two-stage adder adds
binary numbers totalling to a maximum of denary six. A
half adder is suitable for the first adder as there is no
carry from a previous adder.

► The numbers to be added, say, $A_2A_1 + B_2B_1$ are fed into
the four inputs. The first two-digit binary number is applied
to the A inputs and the second to the B inputs. These will
be summed to give a three-bit binary output.

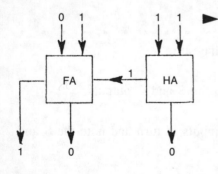

► If denary three (i.e. binary 11) is applied to the A inputs
and denary one (i.e. binary 01) to the B inputs then the
two 1 inputs to HA produce carry but no sum. The 0, 1,
plus a carry 1 on FA produce another carry and no sum.
This makes a binary total of 100 which is denary four.

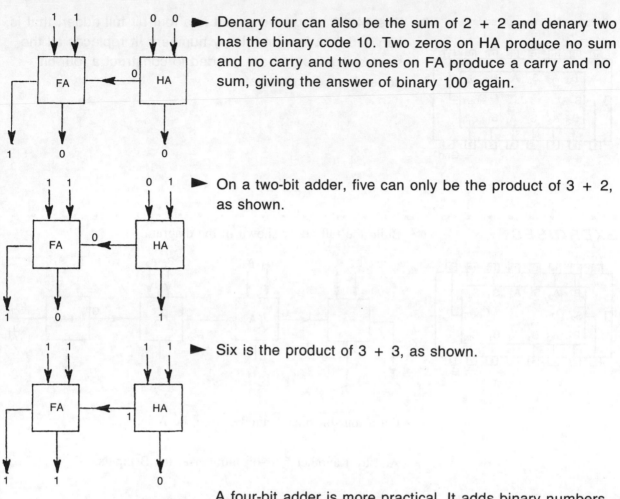

Denary four can also be the sum of 2 + 2 and denary two has the binary code 10. Two zeros on HA produce no sum and no carry and two ones on FA produce a carry and no sum, giving the answer of binary 100 again.

On a two-bit adder, five can only be the product of 3 + 2, as shown.

Six is the product of 3 + 3, as shown.

A four-bit adder is more practical. It adds binary numbers totalling thirty-one using the final carry as a fifth bit output. Usually four full adders are used, only two inputs of the least significant FA being used.

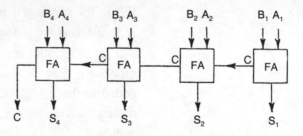

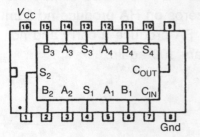

74283 4-bit binary full adder

► The 74283 integrated circuit is a four-bit full adder, that is, can add two, four-bit, binary numbers. It replaces all the separate gates that are needed to construct a four-bit adder from discrete gates.

- -

EXERCISES

► Build the full adder shown in the diagram.

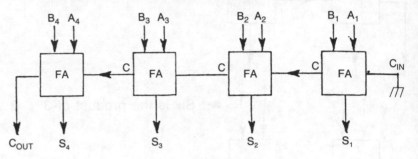

Put a four-bit binary number into the A inputs.

Add to it another four-bit number at the B inputs.

Check the binary number at the S outputs.

Try a few more additions and check the answers.

Fill in the missing words (13).
A four-bit adder is four _____ adders _____. The _____ input is added to the _____ input of FA_1 to produce a _____ and a _____. The _____ is added to the _____ and _____ inputs of FA_2 and so on until a four-bit _____ sum and a _____ has been achieved.

- -

A decimal adder

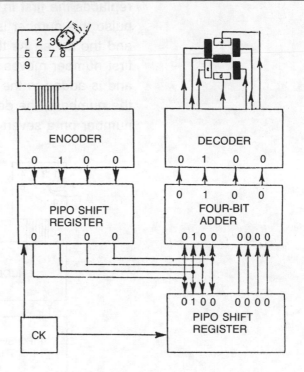

Two decimal numbers can be added together, and displayed as a decimal number, with the circuit shown in the diagram. If a key is pressed, the encoder changes the signal into a binary number and a PIPO shift register stores it. A clock pulse transfers the code to the second eight bit PIPO shift register and also to an adder.

When a second key is pressed, a second binary number replaces the first in the four-bit shift register. After a clock pulse this number is transferred to the eight-bit register and the adder. As this number moves into the register the first number moves across to the B inputs of the adder and is added to the number at the A inputs. After adding the numbers, the decoder decodes it and displays the number on a seven-segment display.

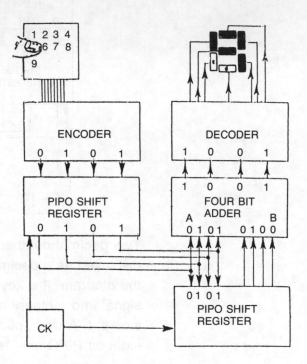

EXERCISES

Build the circuit shown in the diagram.

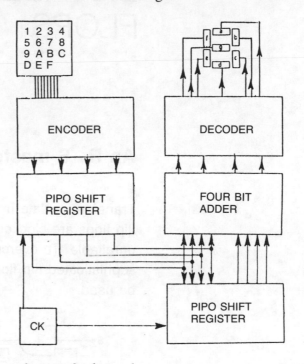

Press a number on the keypad.

Check that the number is in the shift register, using a logic probe.

Pulse the clock once.

Check that the number is in the second shift register.

Repeat the process with a second number.

Check the display shows the sum of the two numbers.

Fill in the missing words (14).
The encoder changes the _____ number from the _____ to a _____ number and the _____ stores it. A _____ transfers the number to another _____ which also stores it. When a second number is moved into this _____ the first number is moved out to the _____ where it is _____ to the second number, decoded and _____.

BISTABLES OR FLIP FLOPS
. . . .

An R–S master–slave flip flop

Transferring data from one flip flop to another when all the flip flops are clocked from the same clock pulse can be unreliable. To overcome this problem, a more sophisticated flip flop called a *master–slave flip flop* can be used.

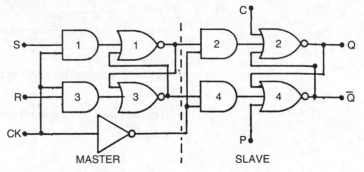

When a logic 1 is applied to the set input of the circuit shown, the first rising clock pulse gives a logic 1 output on AND gate 1 and sends a logic 1 to NOR gate 1. This makes the output of NOR gate 1 logic 0, making the output of NOR gate 3 logic 1. AND gate 4 cannot change state as the NOT gate has inverted the clock pulse. The data has been moved into the master flip flop on the positive clock pulse.

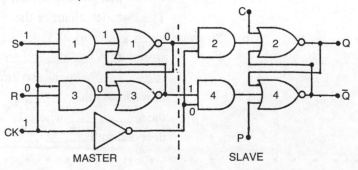

To move the data to the slave flip flop a falling clock pulse is applied. The NOT gate inverts the clock pulse and AND gate 4, and changes the state of NOR gate 4 to make the $\overline{Q}$ output logic 0 and the Q output logic 1. The data has been moved out on a falling clock pulse.

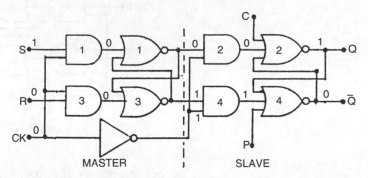

When a logic 1 is applied to the reset input, when coupled with a rising clock pulse, it gives a logic 1 on AND gate 3 output and a logic 0 output from NOR gate 3. Two logic 0s on NOR gate 1 supply a logic 1 to AND gate 2. The data has been moved into the master flip flop.

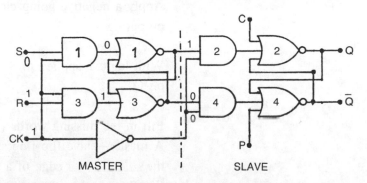

With a falling clock pulse, the NOT gate inverts it and supplies a second logic 1 to AND gate 2 making the input to NOR gate 2 logic 1 and the Q output logic 0. The data has been moved to the slave flip flop.

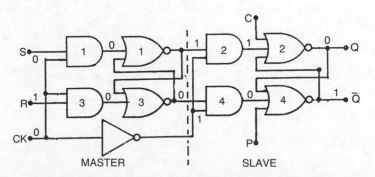

EXERCISES

Build the circuit shown in the diagram. (Note that TTL supplies must not exceed 5 V.)

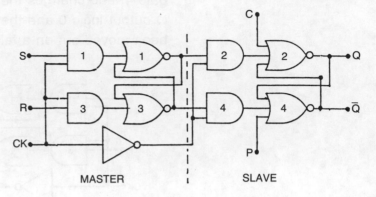

Set the master flip flop with a logic 1 and apply a positive going clock pulse. Note the effect on the Q output.

Check the outputs of the master flip flop and note which AND gate is ready to change logic state.

Apply a negative going clock pulse. Note the effect on the Q output.

With logic 1 applied to S apply a clock pulse and note the effect on Q.

Fill in the missing words (15).
A master–slave flip flop stores data in the master flip flop on the _____ edge of a pulse and transfers data to the slave flip flop on the _____ edge of a pulse. This reduces problems caused by both loading and _____ data on the _____ clock pulse.

T-type master–slave bistables

The *T-type* (toggle) *flip flop* is a modified R–S master–slave flip flop. The Q output is fed back to the R input and the $\overline{Q}$ output is fed back to the S input. If the flip flop is cleared, a logic 0 exists at Q and a logic 1 at $\overline{Q}$ which sets the flip flop.

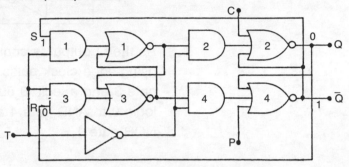

When a logic 1 is applied at T from the clock, AND gate 1 has a logic 1 output and NOR gate 1 supplies a logic 0 to AND gate 2 and a logic 1 to AND gate 4 via NOR gate 3. At this point the inverted T input stops further changes.

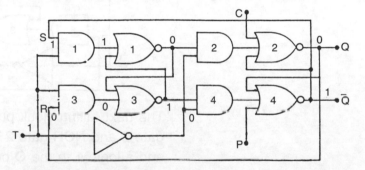

When the falling-edge clock pulse arrives it will invert through the NOT gate and AND gate 4 gives a logic 1 output. NOR gate 4 makes the $\overline{Q}$ output logic 0 and the Q output logic 1.

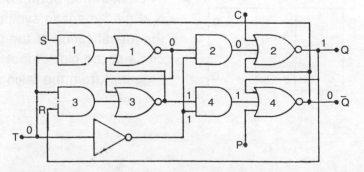

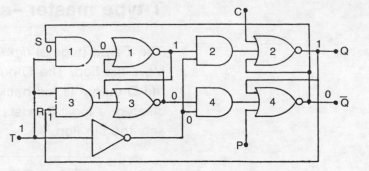

As the Q output is connected to the R input the next rising-edge clock pulse results in a logic 1 output at AND gate 3 and a logic 0 output at NOR gate 3, supplying a logic 0 to AND gate 4 and a logic 1 to AND gate 2, via NOR gate 1.

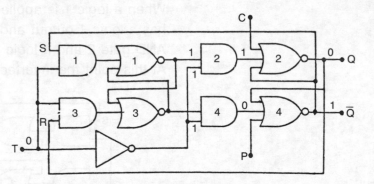

The next falling clock pulse edge inverts to activate AND gate 2 and NOR gate 2 to supply a logic 0 to the Q output and a logic 1 to the Q̄ output. As the R and S inputs are always opposites the flip flop changes with every clock pulse. This is called *toggling*.

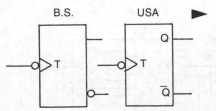

► The difference between the BS 3939 symbol on the left and the American symbol on the right is very slight, only the identification of the Q and Q̄ outputs are different. The circle at the clock input shows that the bistable is triggered from the falling-edge of a clock pulse.

Build the circuit shown in the diagram. (Note that TTL supplies must not exceed 5 V.)

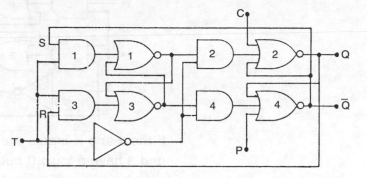

Clear the flip flop using C and apply a clock pulse to the T input. Note the Q and $\bar{Q}$ output logic levels.

Apply a second clock pulse and note the effect on Q and $\bar{Q}$.

Fill in the missing words (16).
A T-type flip flop is the abbreviation of _____ flip flop. If a _____ pulse is applied to the _____ input, the flip flop will _____ or change state continuously, because the _____ and _____ inputs are always opposite to one another.

J–K-type master–slave bistables

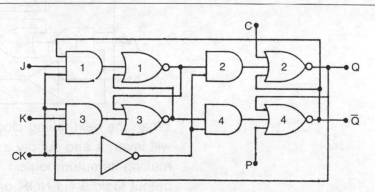

The J–K flip flop is a T-type flip flop with two extra inputs lettered J and K which, like the R and S inputs, pre-determine the Q output after a clock pulse.

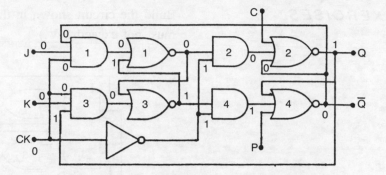

If the J and K inputs are both logic 0, then AND gates 1 and 3 have a logic 0 output and the Q and $\bar{Q}$ outputs do not change even on a changing clock pulse.

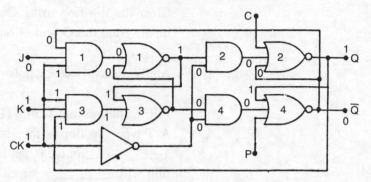

If the K input is preset to logic 1, AND gate 3 output becomes logic 1 with the first rising clock pulse, this makes NOR gate 3 output logic 0 and the output of NOR gate 1, logic 1.

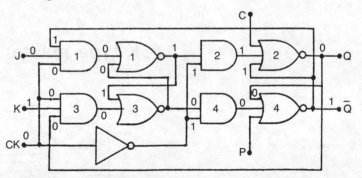

When the next falling clock pulse arrives, the NOT gate will invert it and supply a second logic 1 to AND gate 2, making its output logic 1 which in turn makes the Q output logic 0 via NOR gate 2. Presetting the K input to logic 1 always produces a logic 0 at Q on receipt of a clock pulse. Thus the K input corresponds to the R input of an R−S bistable.

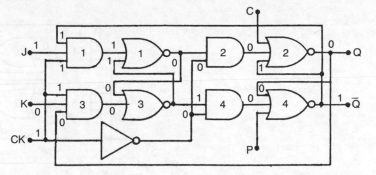

If the J input is preset to logic 1, the first rising clock
pulse gives a logic 1 at AND gate 1 output which in turn
results in NOR gate 1 supplying a logic 0 to AND gate 2
and a logic 1 to AND gate 4, via NOR gate 3.

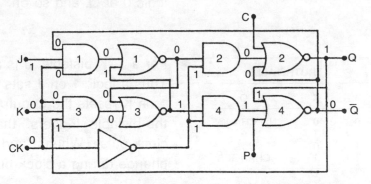

The negative going clock pulse will be inverted by the
NOT gate to supply a second logic 1 to AND gate 4. The
output of this gate is logic 1 which in turn makes the $\bar{Q}$
output logic 0 and the Q output logic 1.

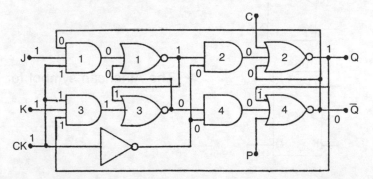

If both J and K inputs are preset to logic 1 the flip flop
reverts back to behaving like a T-type flip flop and causes
toggling. If Q is already logic 1 then AND gate 3 changes
to a logic 1 output, with the rising clock pulse. This makes
the output of NOR gate 3 logic 0 and NOR gate 1 logic 1.

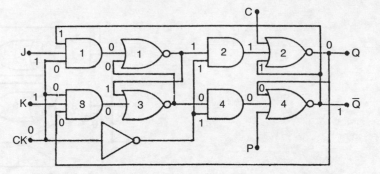

The inverted negative going pulse enables AND gate 2 and NOR gate 2 to change state to give a logic 0 at Q and a logic 1 at $\bar{Q}$.

The next complete clock pulse gives a logic 1 at Q and logic 0 at $\bar{Q}$, and so on.

	TRUTH TABLE	
J	K	Q
0	0	NO CHANGE
0	1	0
1	0	1
1	1	CHANGES

► For a J–K bistable, J is a 'set' input and K a 'reset input'. Thus a logic 1 on J sets the Q output to logic 1 and logic 1 on K resets the Q output to logic 0. When J and K = 1, the bistable 'triggers', that is, changes the Q output on a clock pulse. When J and K = 0, the Q output does not change during a clock pulse.

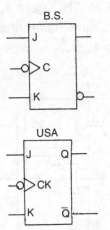

► The diagram shows the British Standards symbol for the J–K flip flop.

► The American symbol for a J–K flip flop is as shown.

74107 Dual J–K Flip Flop

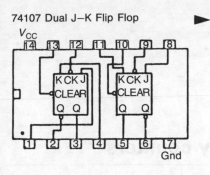

► A range of dedicated integrated circuits are manufactured such as the 74107 J–K flip flop.

· ·

EXERCISES

Build the circuit shown in the diagram. (Note that TTL supplies must not exceed 5 V.)

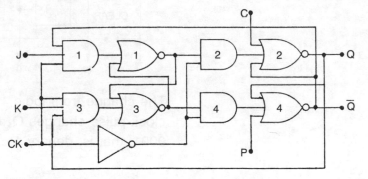

Clear the flip flop by using C and set J and K to logic 0.

Note the Q and $\overline{Q}$ outputs.

Clock the flip flop and check the Q and $\overline{Q}$ outputs.

By changing the J and K logic states, verify the truth table.

Fill in the missing words (17).
The J–K flip flop will not _____ its state unless a logic 1 is applied to the _____ and/or _____ inputs. The flip flop will only toggle with clock pulses when both the _____ and _____ inputs arc logic _____.

· ·

COUNTERS
. . . .

Asynchronous binary counters

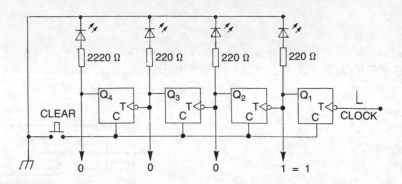

The change from logic 1 to logic 0, (falling-edge), of the clock pulse changes Q_1 to logic 1. This gives a count of 0001, that is, denary 1.

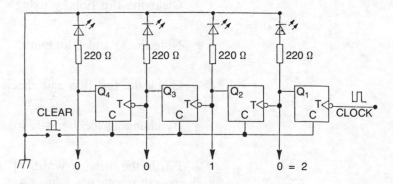

The second falling-edge of the clock pulse causes Q_1 to change to logic 0. Changes in the logic states of Q_2, Q_3 and Q_4 only occur when the preceding Q output changes from logic 1 to logic 0. Thus Q_2 now changes to logic 1, giving a count of 0010, that is, denary 2.

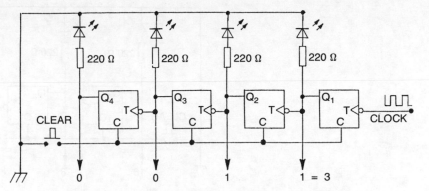

The third falling-edge of the clock pulse causes Q_1 to change to logic 1, but since subsequent changes in Q_2 only occur when Q_1 changes from logic 1 to logic 0, Q_2 remains at logic 1. The count is now 0011, that is, denary 3.

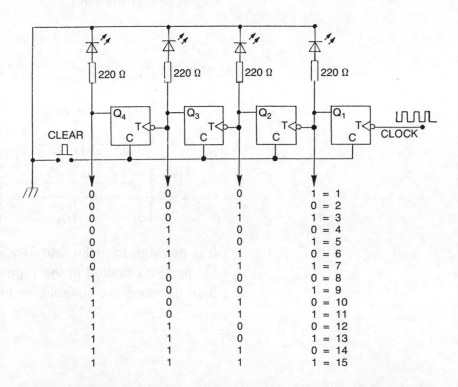

Q_4	Q_3	Q_2	Q_1	
0	0	0	1	= 1
0	0	1	0	= 2
0	0	1	1	= 3
0	1	0	0	= 4
0	1	0	1	= 5
0	1	1	0	= 6
0	1	1	1	= 7
1	0	0	0	= 8
1	0	0	1	= 9
1	0	1	0	= 10
1	0	1	1	= 11
1	1	0	0	= 12
1	1	0	1	= 13
1	1	1	0	= 14
1	1	1	1	= 15

This process continues with successive clock pulses up to a count of 1111, that is, denary 15, as shown in the table. The next clock pulse gives a count of 0000. This type of counter is called a ripple counter.

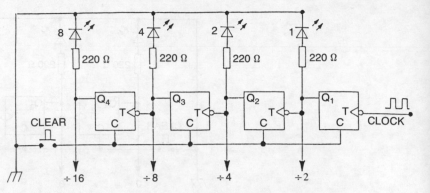

The ripple counter is not an ideal counter for many purposes, as it takes time for the information to ripple through. It is, however, useful when the final count is all that is required. It is also useful for dividing the clock frequency and is sometimes called the *divide-by-sixteen counter* as the Q_4 output is one-sixtheenth the frequency of the clock frequency.

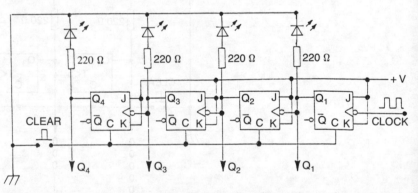

It is possible to make four T-type flip flops from four J−K flip flops connected in the toggle mode. Two 74107 dual J−K flip flops are suitable for the purpose.

Build the circuit shown in the diagram.

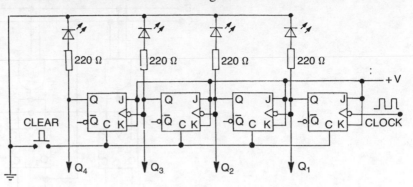

Clear the counter, start the clock and check the count from 0 to 15.

Fill in the missing words (18).
The asynchronous binary counter is often called the _____ counter as binary information _____ through the counter from the first _____ to the last _____. It is also called the divide by _____ counter as the final output is one _____ the frequency of the input.

Synchronous binary counters

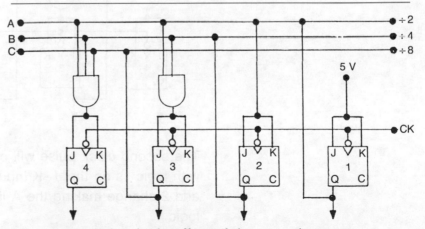

To overcome the ripple effect of the asynchronous counter, a *synchronous counter* can be used as shown in the diagram. It consists of four J–K flip flops and a decoder. The J–K inputs are connected together so that they toggle with the clock pulses.

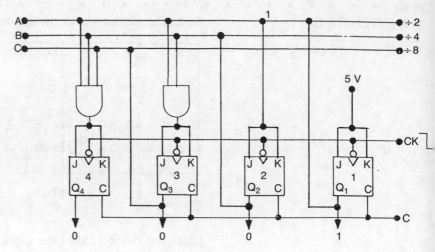

A clear line can be added to set all the Q outputs to logic 0. The first clock pulse sets Q_1 to logic 1. This means that the A line has become logic 1 and flip flops 1 and 2 are set to change on the next clock pulse. The other flip flops will not change as the J−K inputs are at logic 0.

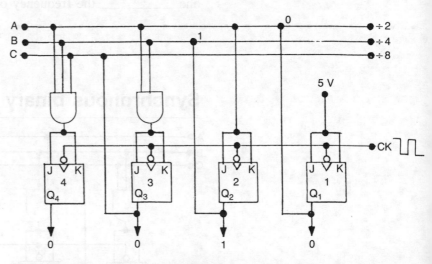

The second clock pulse will change any of the flip flops with logic 1s on the J−K inputs. In this case, flip flops 1 and 2 change making the A line logic 0 and the B line logic 1.

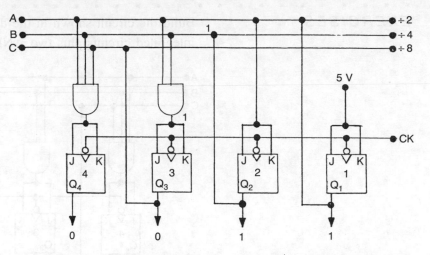

Flip flop 3 only changes when both A and B lines are logic 1 which is on the next clock pulse after the count of 3.

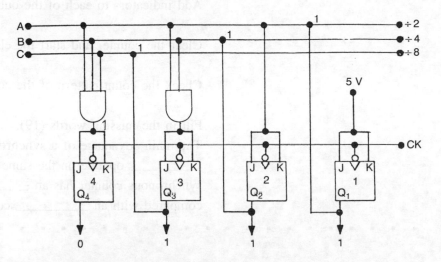

Finally flip flop 4 only changes when all three lines are logic 1, which occurs on the clock pulse after the count of 7. It appears that this counter behaves exactly the same as the asynchronous counter, but because all the flip flops are clocked simultaneously, they do not have to wait for the outcome of a previous change. This results in a counter with an increased counting rate.

EXERCISES

Build the circuit shown in the diagram using two 74101 integrated circuits plus two AND gates.

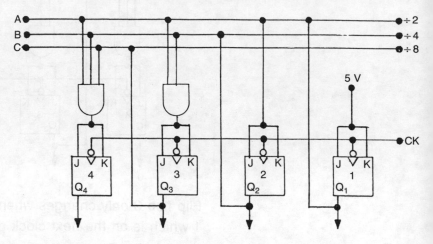

Add indicators to each of the outputs.

Clear the counter and start the clock.

Check the count pattern of the counter.

Fill in the missing words (19).
The main advantage of a synchronous counter is that all of the _____ operate on the same _____. This means that a synchronous counter has an _____ counting rate when compared with an _____ counter.

BCD counters

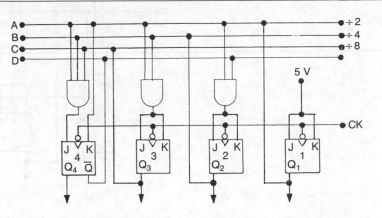

Not all counters count in powers of two. The diagram shows a binary coded decimal (BCD) counter, sometimes called a *decade counter*, which counts from 0 to 9. The circuit has been modified to reduce the count from sixteen different states (0−15), to ten different states (0−9). The number of different states is called the modulus of the counter making this counter a *modulo-10 counter*.

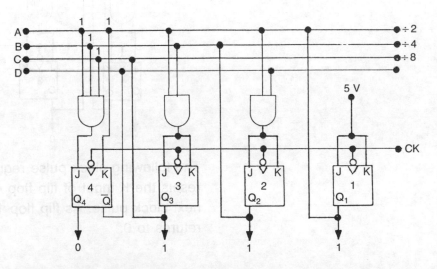

The circuit counts in the normal synchronous way, but when it reaches 7 the J input as well as the K input of flip flop 4 are both logic 1 for the first time so that it will toggle on the next clock pulse making the Q output logic 1 and the Q̄ output logic 0.

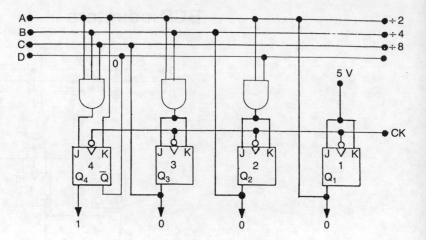

At the same time, the other three flip flops are set for a change, so each one changes from logic 1 to logic 0 on the same clock pulse, making a count of eight.

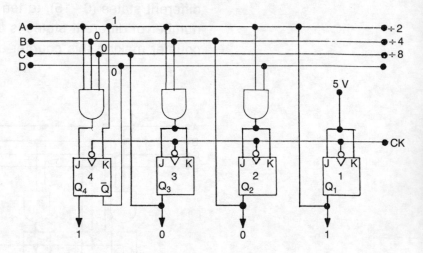

The following clock pulse registers 9 by changing Q_1 and resets the K input of flip flop 4 to change to logic 0 on the next clock pulse. As flip flop 1 also changes, the count returns to 0.

Build the circuit shown in the diagram.

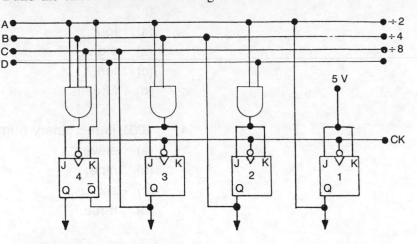

Connect indicators to the outputs.

Clear the counter and start the clock.

Check the count and confirm that the count is . . . . . 7, 8, 9, 0.

Fill in the missing words (20).
A BCD counter is the abbreviation of _____ _____
_____ counter. It is sometimes referred to as a
_____ counter because _____ means ten and the
counter has ten states or _____ ten.

Self-assessment questions

1. SISO is the abbreviation of:
   (a) set input, set output;
   (b) set input, serial output;
   (c) serial input, set output;
   (d) serial input, serial output.

2. Shift registers are made from:
   (a) T-type flip flops;
   (b) D-type flip flops;
   (c) R−S flip flops;
   (d) J−K flip flops.

3. A four-bit shift register will store denary numbers up to:
    (a) four;
    (b) eight;
    (c) ten;
    (d) fifteen.

4. 1001 is the binary number for denary:
    (a) eleven;
    (b) nine;
    (c) six;
    (d) three.

5. A 4 to 16 line decoder is primarily a series of:
    (a) NOT gates;
    (b) NOR gates;
    (c) NAND gates;
    (d) AND gates.

6. PIPO is the abbreviation for:
    (a) preset input preset output;
    (b) parallel input parallel output;
    (c) preset input parallel output;
    (d) parallel input preset output.

7. CMOS gates require a supply of between:
    (a) 5 V and 10 V;
    (b) 3 V and 18 V;
    (c) 3 V and 10 V;
    (d) 10 V and 18 V.

8. A half adder will add denary numbers up to:
    (a) one-half;
    (b) one;
    (c) two;
    (d) three.

9. A synchronous counter is made from:
    (a) T-type flip flops;
    (b) D-type flip flops;

    (c)   R−S flip flops;

    (d)   J−K flip flops.

10.   A BCD counter counts up to:
    (a)   fifteen;
    (b)   ten;
    (c)   nine;
    (d)   four.

Answers to self-assessment questions

1. (d);   2. (b);   3. (d);   4. (b);   5. (d);   6. (b);   7. (b);
8. (d);   9. (d);   10. (c).

Missing words

(1)   Clock pulses, 1, 0, fifteen, four.
(2)   Instantaneously, SISO, one.
(3)   Binary, register, decimal, decoder, decoder, AND, bus, AND, 1, LED.
(4)   Seven, 0, 9, 9, displays.
(5)   Four, binary, clock pulse, clock pulse.
(6)   Nine, binary, Q, inputs, logic 0.
(7)   Encoder, binary, PIPO shift register, register, clock.
(8)   Decimal, binary, shift register, clock, stored, shift register, clock pulse, binary, seven.
(9)   Four-bit binary, manual, binary codes, keyboard or pushbuttons.
(10)   Serial, information, lines, size.
(11)   Exclusive-OR, AND, S, 1, 0, 1.
(12)   Half, OR, three, sum, carry.
(13)   Full, cascaded, A_1, B_1, sum, carry, carry, A_2, B_2, binary, carry.
(14)   Denary, key pad, binary, shift register, clock pulse, shift register, register, adder, added, displayed.
(15)   Rising, falling, transferring, same.
(16)   Toggle, clock, T, toggle, R, S.
(17)   Change, J, K, J, K, 1.
(18)   Ripple, ripples, flip flop, flip flop, sixteen, sixteenth.
(19)   Flip flops, clock pulse, increased, asynchronous.
(20)   Binary coded decimal, decade, decade, modulo.

INDEX